About the Book

Skillfully varied and drawn from many sources, including Chaucer, the legends of the Round Table, and the French *chansons de gestes*, MEDIEVAL TALES will appeal to every taste. Jennifer Westwood has included familiar favorites — Chanticleer the rooster, whose pride was his downfall; Sir Gawain and the Green Knight; the Orpheus legend in medieval dress — and many little known but equally charming stories.

This delightful collection of British and French tales combines a sure feeling for the flavor and color of medieval times with a thoroughly modern verve, freshness, and readability.

The handsome black-and-white drawings, like the text, vividly suggest a medieval tapestry without losing their contemporary humor and zest.

Medieval Tales

Illustrated by Pauline Baynes

MEDIEVAL TALES

Translated and adapted by Jennifer Westwood

Coward-McCann, Inc.   *New York*

First American Edition 1968
Copyright © 1967 by Jennifer Westwood
All rights reserved. This book, or parts thereof, may
not be reproduced in any form without permission in
writing from the publishers.
Library of Congress Catalog Card Number: 68-15657
Printed in the United States of America

Contents

Medieval Tales

The Tale of Chanticleer

Chaucer

ONG AGO, a poor old widow lived with her two daughters in a cottage near a copse. Her worldly wealth was small and yet she had three pigs, three cows, a cross-grained sheep called Moll, and some chickens in the yard as well. This yard was fenced in by a tall stockade with a dry ditch on its outer side, and there the widow kept a valiant cock, by name one Chanticleer, who was the finest crower in the land and far more regular than any clock. Redder than fine coral was his comb and battlemented like a castle wall; his beak was black as jet, his legs sky-blue, his toenails whiter than the lily-flower, his golden feathers brighter than the sun. He was the husband, too, of seven hens, all plump and pretty, but his favourite wife was the fairest of them all by far, the lovely Lady Pertelote.

One dawn, as they were dozing on their perch, the cock began to moan and cry aloud, like someone troubled by an evil dream.

'What ails you, Chanticleer?' cried Pertelote.

'Madam, forgive me,' said the trembling cock. 'I had a dream which so much frightened me that I can feel my heart race even now. Roaming up and down our own backyard there was a sort of hungry, hairy beast, a sort of dog who tried to catch me there, and would have killed me if he could, I have no doubt. His coat was not quite yellow, not quite red, his ears and tail all tipped with coal-black fur, small nose, bright eyes—a nasty sort of beast, enough to make one die upon the spot.'

'For shame, you coward! You have lost my love!' cried Pertelote. 'Where is your manly heart? Everyone knows that dreams are meaningless and come from indigestion, nothing else! Just peck a few herbs growing in the yard—centaury, caper-spurge and hellebore, ground-ivy, laurel and some fumitory, these would I recommend. Your dreams will soon cease then!'

'I thank you for your lore, but in *my* books, I find examples of the truth of dreams. One of our oldest, greatest authors says there were two men who went on pilgrimage and when they reached the town they could not find lodgings together anywhere they went. So they split up and went their separate ways to find whatever resting-place they could. One took his shelter in an ox's stall, and, as it chanced, before the break of day, the other pilgrim dreamed he heard him call:

"Help me! I am in an ox's stall. Tonight I shall be murdered as I lie." The dreamer then awoke, but since he placed no faith in dreams, he went straight back to sleep. Again he dreamed the same, but took no heed, and when the third time came his comrade said:

"Now I am dead. Just see my gaping wounds. Early tomorrow go to the City Gate, and there you'll find a wagon heaped with dung. My body will be hidden in that cart. Arrest its driver and the innkeeper whose stall this is—they killed me for my gold."

The other went to sleep, but when, at dawn, he went down to the ox's stall he found nobody there. The innkeeper came out and quickly said:

"Your friend went early, just before the dawn."

The pilgrim went then, as the dream had said, straight to the City Gate. There stood the cart.

"Help ho!" he cried. "My oldest, truest friend was

murdered here last night and in that cart you'll find his corpse. I saw it in a dream."

The people all ran out and searched the cart, and there, indeed, they found the murdered man. The carter and the innkeeper were seized and tortured soundly till they both confessed. Then they were hanged. 'And in the selfsame book', the cock went on, 'it tells how two young merchants setting out, were kept, by winds against them, in the town around the harbour where their fine ship lay. A few days later, with the evening tide, the wind veered round and they made up their minds to put to sea at dawn on the next day. But in the night, one had a fearful dream. He dreamed a man was standing at his head who bade him wait—'If you put out to sea tomorrow morning, you will both be drowned.' He woke and told his friend all that had passed. The other laughed:

"There is no sense in dreams, and if you stay, you stay alone." And so he took his leave and put to sea. Before he was even half way to his goal, by some strange accident, the ship went down with every man on board and in full sight of every other ship that had put out upon the selfsame tide.

And so you see, my dearest Pertelote, scholars more wise than you believe in dreams. And what about those ancient Israelites, Daniel in the Bible, Joseph too—*they* placed their faith in dreams. Mine bodes me ill, yet how can I be sad while I can see your fair and lovely face?'

With this, he flew down off his bedtime perch and called his wives to peck this seed and that. He thought no more of dreams but sauntered round on tiptoe, the sole monarch of his yard, clucking to his wives and subjects both each time he found a seed.

The Tale of Chanticleer

But on that fair May morning, close at hand, disaster lurked. Behind the cottage, in the little copse, a sly coal-fox had lived for three long years and dined off Chanticleer's ancestral line—his mother, father, and his brothers too, his many cousins umpteen times removed—but never yet had our brave cock himself set eyes on his hereditary foe. The night before, this fox had broken through the high stockade and now he lay concealed amid the cabbage-patch until high noon, waiting just to catch his midday meal. He watched proud Chanticleer strut up and down, and lord it over all his seven wives. Six were basking in the noonday sun and happy in her dust-bath in the sand lay Pertelote, the flower of them all. Chanticleer was singing as he strolled, and idly watching a white butterfly weave up and down and round the cabbage-patch, when suddenly his bright and beady eye met with another, golden, greedy, large, of someone underneath the cabbages. Gone was his glorious song—a faint 'Cok, cok!' was all our rooster managed in his fright. He would have fled away, but even then:

'Oh, Sir! Such haste!' the owner of the eye, none other than the cunning coal-fox, cried. 'Are you afraid of me? Of me, your friend? I only came inside to hear you sing! My lord your father (and your mother too) have visited my house, to my delight! And when it comes to music—I pro-test, there was no music on this earth I loved to hear more than your late, respected father's voice. How hard he strained to keep his eyes shut tight, his head stretched up, on tiptoe as he walked. He had no rival, save perhaps his son.'

So wholly did this flattery succeed, that Chanticleer be-gan to flap his wings, stand right up on his toes, stretch out his neck, shut his eyes fast and crow with all his might. While he was thus engaged, Sir Russell Fox sprang out, attacked, and bore the singer off, and for the moment there was no pursuit.

But the hens, those peerless wives, had seen what dreadful fate had overtaken their beloved lord. Not all the Trojan ladies when Troy fell, nor those of Rome when Nero burned the town, made such an outcry and lament as these! The widow and her daughters heard their noise and, rushing to the door, saw Russell Fox streak back into the copse, with Chanticleer their cock upon his back.

'Ho! Ho! the fox!' and after him they ran, and with them serving-men all armed with sticks. Coll, the dog, and his two brothers ran, and Malkin with her distaff still in hand; the cow ran, and the calf, the three pigs even, in terror at the noise the dogs were making. Men and women shouted, cursed and ran; up flew the frightened geese into the trees, and all the bees came swarming from their hive to join in the pursuit of Chanticleer.

Hearing the din, our valiant cock thought fast. He managed to gasp out.

'If I were you, I would turn round and shout at all these clods: "Turn back! Turn back! The cock is mine for good, now I have reached the safety of the trees." '

Sir Russell Fox, intending to reply, opened his mouth to speak—and lost the cock. The bird at once broke free and flew into the tree-tops with all speed.

'Alas! my Chanticleer!' Sir Russell cried, 'Are you afraid, that thus you fly from me? I meant no harm—come down and I'll explain.'

'No,' said the cock, 'I'd be a pretty dunce if I let you

make a fool of me again! A curse on those who blink when they should look!' And with that, he flew off to his own yard.

'Rather on those who chatter,' said the fox, 'when they should hold their tongues.' And dinnerless he had to slink away.

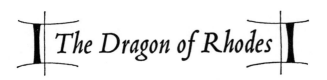

The Dragon of Rhodes

French Romance

The Dragon of Rhodes

ONCE, when the Order of St. John still ruled the distant island we call Rhodes, a fearful dragon came out of the east and wrought great havoc there. By day it lurked up in its mountaincave, savouring poisonous fumes that drifted up from the stagnant marsh far down below; by night it roamed the countryside, destroying all the crops, burning house and cottage with its fiery breath, as it journeyed, seeking out its prey—shepherds, knights errant, lonely travellers.

The people of the island begged the knights belonging to the Order of St. John to rid them of the cause of all their woe. Many brave men undertook the task. One by one, they set out for the hills, but none returned and no word came back. The Grand Master of the Order at long last, forbade his knights to undertake the quest and the dragon raged unhindered as before.

But there was among them one young knight, Sir Theodore, a native of Provence, whose greatest dream was to achieve some quest and so win fame. What better quest than this where all had failed? For long he had been pondering how to kill the dragon that persecuted Rhodes, and now he asked the Grand Master for leave to go back for a time to his old home. There he found a craftsman who could make a dragon for him, fashioned out of wood. With his father's warhorse and two dogs, the young knight practised with his wooden foe each day till he was sure that he had found at last the perfect way to kill the real beast. Then taking horse and dogs, he sailed for Rhodes and straightway set out on the long ascent which led up to the dragon's fiery lair.

The dogs threw back their heads and loudly howled to draw the dragon out—and out he came. But he was breath-ing snaky tongues of fire which seared the grass around the horse's feet. Accustomed to a monster made of wood, the great war-horse took fright, reared, threw his rider, wildly fled, careering down the rocky mountain-side. Sir Theo-dore got quickly to his feet, shaken and bruised, thinking his end had come for the dragon was advancing step by step. But he found the dogs still standing there, waiting for his word. He gave it, and at once the brave dogs leaped straight at the dragon's head and held on tight, sinking their teeth into the glittering scales which spread like wings at each side of its neck. Maddened with pain, it reared high in the air, bearing the mastiffs with it, clinging fast, and as it did so, Theodore advanced and thrust his lance deep in its scaleless breast until it reached the heart. Crashing down on him the dragon came, but when his squires dragged him from underneath, he was unhurt and his foe was dead.

The news of victory spread far and wide, and all the people of the city swarmed joyfully around him as he went to tell the Master what he had achieved. With the faithful mastiffs running close behind his heels, he strode into the great assembly-hall and down between long ranks of silent knights clad in their black cloaks with the silver cross, the emblem of the Order of St. John. He laid his sword down at the Master's feet expecting to receive his thanks and praise, but the old man's face was grave and sad.

'What does our order ask of every knight? What virtue does it prize above the rest?' he asked the young knight sternly.

'Obedience,' Theodore replied, and hung his head for shame. Had he not disobeyed the strict command that none should fight the dragon in the hills?

'Your life is spared,' the Master said, 'because you have saved Rhodes. But because you broke the solemn vow of obedience which you made me as a knight, you are banished from this Order and this land.'

The punishment seemed harsh to those who heard, but Theodore himself made no complaint. He thought:

'I broke my vow, and all for a moment's fame. Now must I pay, and forfeit up the thing that in all the world I held most dear—my knighthood and the company of knights.'

In silence he took off his own black cloak and laid it sadly down beside the sword. He bowed and turned to leave the well-known hall and all his friends for the last time, never to return. But just as he had reached the outer door, the voice of the Grand Master rang out clear:

'Knight of St. John, your obedience is proved, because you did not question your harsh doom. Return, my son, you may reclaim your cloak. Be the defender of the isle of Rhodes as long as your life lasts.'

And he was. The young knight of Provence lived out his days in Rhodes, and in his turn was Master of the Order of St. John. When he died, an old and famous man, the people of the island set a stone above his grave, on which they carved in golden characters:

'Here lies the Dragon's Vanquisher.'

The Nightingale

The Nightingale

NEAR ST MALO, there was once a town where two rich barons lived, one young, one old. The younger was the foremost of all men in graciousness and goodness, virtue, skill, and in the tournament he had no peer. But he lacked one thing which the other had—a wife so beautiful and courteous there was no lady in the land more fair. The young man loved her, and he told her so. She, knowing his great merit, loved him too. Their houses stood together, side by side, with only a high wall to come between. If she stood at her casement, he at his, they could converse for hours across the wall. They would have asked no more—they were content.

But one year, when the fields and woods were green, and birds were clinging to the flower-heads, piping their sweet songs, the young man grew more love-sick than before. At his persuasion, the old baron's wife would now rise up at night, put on a cloak and from her moonlit window watch for him. And when he came, they stood for hours and gazed, just as they had by day. At last her husband asked her what she did, as she stood by her window every night.

'There is a nightingale that sings so sweet, I cannot sleep until he goes away,' the lady said.

He laughed most cruelly, and set his servants all to making traps which they then hung up in the orchard-trees. It was not very long before these snares enmeshed a helpless, hapless nightingale. They brought it in alive to the old man, who took it to the lady in her bower.

'Here is the wretch who keeps you from your sleep,' he said, 'and you will get more peace when he is dead.' With that, he killed the bird from cruelty, and flung it at his wife. She held the poor thing in her hands and wept, not only for the bird but for herself. No more at her casement could she stand and watch for the young baron in the night. How could she tell him that she might not come? If she sent no message, he would think that she no longer loved him. What to do?

She wrote a letter on a piece of silk and wrapped it round the bird. Then choosing out a servant she could trust, she sent the little body to her love. He read the letter, learned all that had passed, and knew with that, that now their joy must end. She could no longer stand and gaze at him nor he at her, for their excuse was gone. He had a box made out of gold and gems, and in it put the little nightingale. He sealed it tightly and from that day forth, he kept it always by him, till he died, in memory of the love that he had lost.

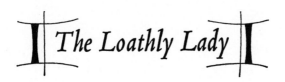

The Loathly Lady

Chaucer

I

N THE DAYS when Arthur was the king, and fairies were still living in this land, it happened that a young and gallant knight broke one of the Round Table's strictest rules and was condemned to die. So earnestly the Queen begged for his life that Arthur granted it, and placed him in her hands for punishment. Then she said to the knight:

'I will spare your life if in return you answer me this question—"What is it that women most desire?" I give you leave to go and journey through the land, but if you cannot tell me in a year and a day, then you must surely die!'

The knight was resolved to leave the court at once, and he set out on his quest hoping that he would have learned the answer long before the year came to an end. In villages and towns, in the dwellings of the poor, in the castles of the rich he made enquiry then, but nowhere could he find two people who agreed. Some said what women most desired was wealth, honour or pleasure, some said splendid clothes. While many of them thought that flattery was the thing that they liked best, others said no, they all longed to be called steadfast and true, prudent, loyal or wise. The year's end fast approached, but no nearer was the knight to answer-ing the question of the Queen. At last the day arrived when he should return to court, and he turned homeward gloom-ily, expecting only death.

As he was riding slowly down the forest-lanes, he saw a company of ladies dancing on the grass. So fair of face and light of foot were they, he knew they must be fairies and so wise they would be sure to know an answer which could save his life. But as he drew near them eagerly, they

vanished every one, leaving behind nothing save a crone, ugly as sin, still sitting on the grass. This hideous old creature now arose, and coming forward to his stirrup said:

'Sir Knight, this road leads nowhere. Tell me what troubles you and what you seek. The old are often wise and the ugly still do much to help.'

'I must die for certain,' said the knight, 'unless I solve this riddle by tonight—"What is it that women most desire?" If you can tell me this I vow that I will give to you whatever you require.'

'Only swear to me that you will grant the next thing that I ask, and you shall know the answer before night.'

'I swear,' said the young knight.

'Then you are saved,' said she. 'The Queen must needs agree with the answer you will give.'

She whispered a few words in his ear and they went on their way.

Many ladies had assembled at the court to hear the Queen pass sentence on the knight. He was led into the presence of them all and the question was asked him by the Queen:

'What is it that women most desire?'

The knight gave his reply with confidence and in the hearing of the whole court said:

'Madam, the thing that women most desire is to gain mastery over men.'

In all King Arthur's court there was no lady who denied the truth of what he said, and now they all declared that he had earned his pardon. At this, the crone got up and hobbled to the Queen:

'Madam, it was I who taught him to say this, and in

[28]

return he swore that he would grant the next thing that I asked of him. Now I demand he take me as his wife, for I have rescued him from certain death. This can he not deny.'

'Alas!' cried the poor knight, 'that was indeed my vow. Ask anything but that! Take all my lands and wealth but let me go!'

'Not for all the world would I forego the right to be your wife,' was all she said.

And so, in grief of heart, he married the old crone but did it secretly because he could not bear the court to mock him for his loathly bride.

'Is it the fashion of King Arthur's court to treat a new wife thus?' the crone enquired. 'I saved your life and yet you keep me hidden from your friends at Arthur's court! Where is your gratitude? Have *I* done anything to cause you grief? If so, pray tell me so that I can make amends.'

'Amends!' exclaimed the knight. 'What amendment can there be for low degree and age and ugliness? I am the laughing-stock of all the court!'

'Is that your whole complaint?' enquired the crone.

'Is it not enough?' the knight replied.

'If I but chose,' she said, 'I could amend all this before three days were out. But you must learn the folly of your pride. What is degree? And what is rank or state? He is noble who does noble deeds. And as for age, is not this the time of greatest wisdom, to be reverenced? Since I am old and hideous besides, you will not live in dread of losing me to some other knight. Choose therefore, which of these things you will—to have me old and true, or a young and fair and faithless wife?'

[29]

The knight was puzzled. Which one should he choose? He thought hard for a while, then sighed and said:

'My dear wife, choose whichever pleases you.'

'Then I have gained the mastery over you!' the crone exclaimed.

'So be it,' said the knight, 'with your decisions shall I rest content.'

'To you, therefore, I shall be young *and* true.'

And as she spoke these words, he turned around. Before him now no loathly lady stood, but in her place one young and beautiful! No words can tell what love between them grew, and they lived happily to their lives' end.

The Knight with the Two Swords

A MESSENGER once came to Arthur's court when it was held in London, bring-ing news that Rience of North Wales had summoned up a mighty host, intending to wage war upon the King, and was ravaging his borders even now.

'It were a shame to me and all of us, if this prince went unopposed,' King Arthur said. And so a general summons was sent out, bidding every baron, knight and squire to rally to the King at Camelot, to hold a council there, and also jousts.

When the King had gone there with his court, a damsel entered in his hall one day, sent from the Lady Lile of Avelion. As she drew back her mantle, edged with fur, they saw that she was girded with a sword. The King, astonished, asked her why she wore a thing so unbecoming to her sex.

'Lord,' said the damsel, 'none but a gallant knight, free from treason and all villainy can draw this sword. Such a one I seek, that I may be delivered from this plight. I have been to the court of Rience of North Wales, because I heard that he had valiant knights, yet though they all assayed, not one could draw it out.'

'This is a strange affair if it be true,' said Arthur, 'and I will be the first to try my skill, not thinking that *I* am the best of knights, but as example to these noble lords.'

He tugged and pulled amain, but the sword stayed in the sheath.

'You need not pull so hard,' the damsel said, 'he that shall draw it shall need little might.'

'Let all my barons try,' King Arthur said. Yet though they came in turn none could succeed.

It happened at that time there was a knight, poor but a man of valour and prowess, who had been Arthur's prisoner half a year, for slaying the King's cousin in a fight. The barons had secured him his release and he was present in the royal hall when all these things befell. In his heart he felt he could succeed though others failed, yet since he was in such poor garments clothed, he held back in the crowd and would not try. The damsel had begun to take her leave when this knight, Balin, called to her and said:

'Damsel, I pray you of your courtesy, allow me to assay as these lords have.' The damsel looked at him and his poor clothes. He seemed without distinction or prowess.

'Put me to no more trouble, Sir, I pray you seem unlikely to succeed where these lords failed.'

'Ah! fair damsel,' said the worthy knight, 'virtue and good deeds are not in clothes but hidden in the man.'

'You speak true,' said the damsel, 'therefore try.'

Then Balin held her girdle with its sheath and drew the sword out from it easily. The whole court marvelled, and the damsel said:

'This is the best knight that I ever found, and many are the brave deeds he shall do. Now courteous knight, give me the sword again.'

'No,' said Balin, 'this sword will I keep, unless you take it back again by force.'

'You are not wise to keep the sword from me,' the damsel said, 'for with it you shall slay your dearest friend.'

'I will take the fate that God ordains, but the sword you shall not have,' said Balin then, and the damsel went away.

Soon after this, the knight sent for his horse and took
his leave of Arthur. Said the King: 'Will you leave our
company so soon? Is it that you are displeased with me?
The blame for your imprisonment does not lie at my door,
for I was misinformed. I did not know your valour and
prowess. Now you are free stay with me in my court. I will
reward you then as you deserve.'

'Your bounty is too great for tongues to tell,' said Balin.
'I thank you for it yet I must depart.'

While the knight was arming, to the court the Lady of
the Lake, in rich array, came proudly riding. She greeted
Arthur, and then asked the gift that he had promised her
when first she gave him bright Excalibur.

'Ask what you will,' said Arthur. 'You shall have it if it
lies within my power.'

'I ask the head of him who won the sword, or else the
damsel's head who brought it here. Either or both. Balin
slew my brother, a good knight, and the damsel caused my
father's death.'

'Ask something else,' said Arthur, 'because this I cannot
grant.'

'I crave nothing but this,' the Lady said.

As Balin was about to leave the court, he saw the Lady
of the Lake and learned that she had asked his head.

'You would have my head, therefore lose yours,' he said,
and lightly cut her head off where she stood.

'You have shamed me and my court,' King Arthur cried.
'I was indebted to that lady, who was here with my safe-
conduct. I shall not forgive you this fell deed.'

'I am grieved at your displeasure,' Balin said, 'for this
same lady has slain many knights by witchcraft and

[34]

enchantment. She it was whose falsehood caused my mother to be burned.'

'Whatever cause you had,' said Arthur then, 'here in my house you should have stayed your hand. Get you gone from this court with all speed.'

So Balin left the court, with this intent, to conquer Rience, make him prisoner and thus win back his lord King Arthur's grace. When he had gone, Merlin came to court, and Arthur told him what had taken place.

'As for the damsel girded with the sword,' said Merlin, 'she was in league with Lady Lile to slay the damsel's brother; by her test she sought to find a gallant knight to do the deed. But he who won that sword shall not live long. It grieves me much—there is no knight of more prowess than he.'

As Balin was riding on his way, he turned towards a forest, where he saw a knight who bore his brother Balan's arms. Balan it was, indeed, and when they met, they both took off their helms and wept for joy. Then Balan said:

'I little thought that I would meet you here, though I had heard that you were free again. I was riding to the court to look for you.'

Balin told his brother of the sword, and how he killed the Lady of the Lake.

'I am much grieved now at King Arthur's wrath,' said Balin. 'I would place my life in jeopardy to win his love again. Will you come to Castle Terrabil which Rience holds at siege, and against him prove our honour and prowess?'

'We shall help each other as brothers ought to do,' Sir

[35]

Balan said. On the way, they met with Merlin in disguise and did not know him.

'Where do you ride to?' Merlin asked.

'It is no concern of yours,' replied the knights.

'But what is your name,' said Balin.

'At this time I will not tell you,' Merlin said.

'You are no true man if you will not speak your name.'

'That is as it may be,' Merlin said, 'but I can tell you why you ride this way. You go to meet King Rience, but unless you have my counsel you will fail.'

'Ah!' said Balin, 'you must be Merlin then. We will be ruled by you.'

'Come on,' said Merlin, 'and win glory there. But look first to your valour. You will have great need.'

'Do not fear,' said Balin, 'we will do what we may.'

Merlin hid them in a wood beside the road, the horses grazed, the knights lay down to rest. About midnight, he made them rise again, and arm themselves for Rience was nearby.

'Which is the King?' asked Balin. Merlin said:

'Here in this narrow place, you three shall meet.' He showed the brothers where the King would ride. Balin and Balan met with Rience there and struck him down with forty of his men. They would have slain the King as well as these, had he not yielded and sued for grace.

'Do not slay me, valiant knights,' he cried, 'my life will profit you, but not my death.'

'You speak the truth,' the two knights said, and on a litter carried him to court. Merlin had vanished, and already come to Arthur, telling him the tale.

'By whom was Rience vanquished?' Arthur asked.

[36]

'By two knights who would please you,' Merlin said. 'You shall learn their names tomorrow when they come.'

But the brothers left King Rience at the castle gate, giving him in charge of porters there, while they two turned again in the dawning of the day. King Arthur came to Rience where he lay.

'Sir, you are welcome. But who captured you?' he said.

'Two brothers,' said King Rience, 'and one was a knight who had two swords.'

'I do not know them, yet I owe them much.' Merlin said:

'I tell you that the one knight is Balin, who won his second sword here in your court; the other is Balan—I grieve for him that he shall not live long.'

The brothers parted company and rode their separate ways, and many an adventure befell them on the road. It happened one day, that Balin passed by a cross, and on it was written in golden characters: 'Toward this castle no knight shall ride alone!' An old man was standing there:

'You pass your bounds to come this way. Turn again, Balin. It will be for your good.'

He straightway vanished, and Balin heard a horn, blown as it might be for a hunted beast.

'That blast,' said Balin, 'is surely blown for me. I am the kill, and yet I am not dead.'

Then he saw a hundred ladies, and with them many knights, who led him to their castle and entertained him there with dancing and minstrelsy and apparent joy. But then the chief lady of the castle came to him.

'Knight with the Two Swords,' the lady said, 'you must

[37]

joust with the knight who guards the isle. No man may pass this way unless he does.'

'That is an evil custom,' Balin said, 'to give what seems a welcome, all for this.'

'There is but one to fight with,' she replied.

'If I have to, I am ready,' Balin said.

'Sir,' said a knight, 'your shield seems weak to me. I will lend you a bigger one.' Balin took the shield that was unknown, and left the one which bore his own device. He rode down to the river, and in a boat both he and his horse with him crossed to the other side. He met a damsel on the island, and seeing him, she cried:

'Why have you left your own shield, and put yourself in danger, for you would have been known by it.'

Said Balin: 'I am sorry that I came into this country, but I cannot turn for shame. I shall take what may befall.'

From the castle before him a knight in red came riding. When this knight saw the two swords, he thought it must be Balin, his own brother, but the shield was strange to him and he supposed that it could not be he. They lowered their spears and galloped at each other, and such was their encounter that they both fell to the ground. They rose and struck each other. Weary was the combat, the wounds they gave were grievous, and the field was red with blood before Balan laid him down.

'What knight are you?' said Balin. 'You are the first to match me.'

'Balan is my name,' the other said, 'my brother is the Knight with the Two Swords.'

Balin fell back fainting on the ground. Balan crawled to where his brother lay, took off his helm, yet did not know his face, it was so gashed and dripping with his blood. Balin awoke, and weeping, said:

'Balan, my brother, thou hast slain me and I thee.'

'Alas that I should ever see the day when through chance I did not know you,' Balan said. 'I saw the two swords but you bore another shield, and so I thought you were a stranger knight.'

'A knight of the castle made me take this shield,' said Balin. 'If I were to live, I would destroy that castle for its crimes.'

'That were well done,' said Balan. 'When I came, I chanced to slay the knight who kept this isle, and had to take his place. You would have taken mine if you could have saved your life.'

The lady of the castle came to them with all her people. Balan prayed that she would bury both in the same tomb.

'When we are dead, have written over us how brothers slew each other by mistake. Never a good knight or good man will pass, without a prayer for our most wretched souls.'

Balan died there; Balin the next midnight, and both were buried in the selfsame tomb. The lady wrote how Balan, the good knight, lay slain there by his only brother's hand, for she did not know what Balin might be called. But Merlin came next morning, and in letters of gold wrote: 'Balin lies here, the Knight with the Two Swords.'

Sir Launfal

Metrical Romance

Sir Launfal

AT THE COURT OF ARTHUR long ago, there was no knight more generally beloved than young Sir Launfal. The ladies loved him for his looks and the knights for his great valour, but the poor people of the city loved him best for his warmhearted gen⁄erosity. He had one enemy, however, and that a powerful one—Queen Guinevere, the King's own wife. She hated the young knight because he would not say that she was the fairest in the land, and so she schemed to bring about his ruin. She whispered lies into King Arthur's ear until the time came when he would not pay Sir Launfal for his service with rich gifts nor give him treasure as the meed of valour as he had done before. Yet still the knight gave with a liberal hand to all who asked, so that at last his coffers were all emptied. Then his former friends melted away, like snow before the sun, his servants left him and the poor ceased to bless his name, for by now he had no more than they. The mayor of the town, in whose house he lodged, seized all his furniture as rent and bade him be gone, if he could no longer pay. All that he had left was a rusty coat of mail and a tired old horse that could scarcely walk, and with these he crept quietly out of town early one morning before anyone was stirring, so that none should see him in his shame.

He travelled on, leading his old horse, until towards mid⁄day he reached the forest⁄eaves, and there he sat beneath a tree to shelter from the heat of noon, letting the horse graze and hoping that the lush, green grass would fill out its spare frame. He had not been sitting there for long, lost in his gloomy thoughts, when suddenly, to his surprise, he

saw two damsels coming through the trees, one with a
silver basin, the other with a towel. They greeted him with
courtesy and gently washed his hands, then bade him follow
them to where their mistress was.

'Gladly will I follow,' Launfal said, 'not the Queen and
all her ladies are so fair!'

'Not till you see our mistress will you know what beauty
is,' was their reply, and the more eagerly did he follow them
through thicket and through glade, till all at once a strange
sight met his eyes. There in the midst of the wild and lonely
wood, the haunt of savage men and of enchanted beasts, a
fair pavilion stood, for all the world as if upon a peaceful
plain at some great tournament. Of shimmering silk it was,
with silver tassels and on top, a golden eagle glittering in the
sun, and yet it did not shine so bright as the long yellow
hair of a lady, who in Launfal's eyes seemed fairer than the
sun itself. His heart followed his eyes and became her slave.
He knew that he could love no woman in the world now
he had seen *her* perfect loveliness.

'Sir,' said the lady then, 'you are no stranger to me. I
have heard of you and known your worth for many months.
Now I have sent for you to ask if you think me fair enough
to wed.'

'Most gracious lady,' stammered the young knight, scarce
able to believe what he had heard, 'what greater joy could
any man desire? But I am poor and friendless and despised.
What can I offer you?'

'I know all this,' the lady said, 'but if you freely give
your heart to me, I can make you rich as any king, for I
have wealth at will.'

There was no need to ask him if he loved her! She made

him sit beside her in all his rags and rust, while her maidens brought a table spread with food. But half-starved though he was, he had eyes only for her. The hours flew like minutes as they talked, and all too soon, it seemed to him, the lady said:

'And now you must return to Arthur's court, and I shall give you wealth enough to shame all those who scorned you, being penniless.'

She gave him gifts at parting—first a suit of pure white armour, marvellously made, next a magic purse that he could never empty, spend as he might, and then, best of all, the promise they should meet.

'But,' said the lady, 'one thing I require, that you tell no mortal of our love. Call to me in some secret place and I shall come, but if you speak of me to human ears, you shall never see me more on earth.'

Sir Launfal swore by all his knightly vows that he would obey her, for it seemed an easy pledge to keep. Then, mounting the white steed which her damsels brought to him, he galloped like the wind off to the town.

When he reached his former dwelling-place, he found a multitude of servants waiting there for his arrival, and rich furnishings where none had been before. He knew for certain that his lady was a fairy-woman by whose magic arts all this had come about. From the enchanted purse there ran an endless stream of gold with which he fed the poor and ransomed prisoners, gave alms to pilgrims and rewarded minstrels for their songs. Rich gifts were given to followers and friends, who soon flocked back now that his shame was past and money freely flowing. Once more his name was spoken everywhere with gratitude and love, and once more Guinevere was grieved that it should be so.

On the feast of St. John, when knights and ladies gathered in the meadow before the castle to dance on the green grass, the Queen came there with her handmaidens to join in the revelries. When she saw that Launfal did not dance, but walked apart, daydreaming of his love, she spoke scornfully, saying he was not fit to serve the King since no woman found him worthy of her love. Sir Launfal's pride was stung and, forgetting all the promises he made, he cried:

'Madam, it is not so! Know that I am loved by the fairest lady in the land!'

'Sir Knight, how dare you speak of one more fair than I, and to my face!' exclaimed the Queen.

'The least of her handmaidens is more beautiful than you,' replied the angry knight, and at once his snow-white armour turned as black as coal. All too late thought Launfal of his vow!

Guinevere in anger left the dance, and, weeping and raging, went in to her lord. With red-rimmed eyes and hair in disarray, she made demand that punishment be given for this insult. False and shameful charges then she made which moved the King to anger, and he sent four sergeants out to make the knight their prisoner. To Launfal now, the King's displeasure seemed a trifle set beside the greater grief that had befallen him. Once again the knight was destitute. His purse was empty and his servants gone, his lodgings bare as they had been before. His lady gave no answer to his call in the forest where they used to meet. The charm was broken!

Sir Launfal

When he was led before the royal throne, he was sternly questioned by the King:

'What are these vaunts you have been heard to speak, that your own love is fairer than my Queen?'

'What I have said is true,' replied the knight, 'and I shall not gainsay it.'

'Then let him hang!' screamed Guinevere, and forthwith Arthur named twelve lords to sit in judgement on the knight. But knowing the pride and falseness of the Queen, most of them pitied him, and when the day came for him to stand trial, one of the older lords began to speak:

'Launfal is standing trial here today for naming his lady fairer than the Queen. Therefore let him bring his lady here, that we may judge if he has spoken true.'

All readily agreed, save Guinevere, but Launfal knew his lady would not come in answer to his call, and men began to say that he must hang. But even as the judges cast their votes, two maidens, in rich samite clad, entered the hall and knelt before the King. They told him there approached a great princess, their mistress, who desired him to receive her. Arthur ordered noblemen to attend the maidens and escort their mistress in, but meantime the trial must proceed, so eager was the Queen to see Sir Launfal dead.

At last the lords were ready to pass sentence, but at that moment, the trumpets rang outside, heralding the coming of their guest. She was riding on a milk-white steed and on her wrist a hooded falcon sat, as token of her high and noble birth, while at her horse's heels, there ran two grey-hounds of the finest breed, lissome and light of foot. She wore a silver robe and a cloak of purple silk, bordered with

ermine, and upon her head a coronet of gold and gems. All
the people of the town ran out to see her pass, and when she
came into the hall, the whole assembly rose to honour her,
for never had such loveliness been seen.

Well did Sir Launfal know her, and he cried:

'Lady, my grief is past now that we meet again.'

But she passed proudly by, and gave him not a word.
She mounted the dais where sat Guinevere with all her
maidens, and they paled before her beauty as the moon and
stars grow dimmer at the rising of the sun. Standing beside
the Queen, the stranger turned, and speaking to the judges,
she declared:

'Sirs, you do wrong to punish this good knight, for you
may see that he is not at fault. Judge for yourselves which of
us is most fair.'

With one accord the judges all exclaimed that she was
the fairest lady in the land, and even Arthur said she had
no peer. Launfal had spoken true. He was set free, but
little cared he then, for when the lady took her leave, without a word or look she passed him by and now was riding
through the city-gates. Sir Launfal's horse stood outside the
hall, and in despair he leaped upon its back and galloped
after her, crying all the while that she should speak to him
if but one word. Never an answer gave she, but rode
swiftly on until they reached a river, wide and deep. There
she dismounted and plunged into the stream. Mail-clad
though he was, the knight pursued, farther and farther out to
where the current ran most strong. The waters closed above
the lady's head and the despairing knight flung himself forward in a last attempt to grasp her shining robe. The
current dragged him down, bore him away, and with the

water ringing in his ears, he gave himself up for dead. But at the moment when all hope was lost, the lady turned and caught him in her arms, bearing him away to fairyland. When he returned to life he saw the flowery bank on which he lay and then the long gold hair of his true love as she bent over him. She told him that she had forgiven him, and they should be parted nevermore.

Sir Launfal was not seen on earth again, but ever since that day, his gallant horse has roamed the land and each year on that date comes to the self-same river-bank and neighs and tears the turf up in the place where his beloved master disappeared.

The Three Young Men and Death

Chaucer

The Three Young Men and Death

THERE WERE ONCE THREE YOUNG MEN who led a riotous life, drinking and revelling the night away with never a care in the world except how to be happy. One day as they sat in the tavern, they heard the hand-bell ringing, before a coffin on its way to the graveyard, and they straightway shouted to the little pot-boy to run outside and see who was being buried that day.

'I can tell you that without stirring a foot,' said he, 'for I was told the news a good two hours since. One of your friends was struck down where he sat, on a tavern-bench. Dead drunk he was, and a thief called Death, who kills off all the folks round here, came up and stabbed him to the heart. He's killed a thousand in the present plague, and more, so you had best be wary and watch out for him.'

At this the keeper of the tavern chimed in:

'What the lad says is true. Death lives in a big village no more than a mile away, and *there* he has killed everyone—men, women, children, serfs, the lot.'

Then one of our three revellers exclaimed:

'This fellow Death can't be so fierce that he will tackle three at once. Come, we'll make a vow to kill him, now, this very night, as he has killed our friends. Death himself shall die!'

They swore eternal brotherhood, then staggered off in drunken rage towards the village where Death was said to be.

They had not gone more than half their journey, when they came to a stile, and there they saw a poor old man, bent with the weight of years and clad in rags.

'God bless you and give you peace,' quavered the old man.

'Out of the way, you old fool,' snapped the proudest of the three, 'what are your blessings to us? Why are you so muffled up we can only see your face? Why do you bother to live so long, why not just go and die?'

The old man sighed.

'Though I have walked to India and back,' he said, 'I have never found a single man, in village or in town, who would exchange *his* youth for *my* age. And as for dying, not Death himself will slay me. Alone I walk the ground, my mother's gate, knocking with my staff from morn to night, crying "Mother, open to me soon and let me in." But she will not. It does you great dishonour thus to mock an old man who has done you no offence. Better to revere another's age as you might wish for reverence in your turn— if you live long enough.'

He made as if to leave.

'You shall not go,' said one of the revellers, 'for you mentioned Death who destroys all fine young fellows hereabouts, and from your age and aspect you must surely be his spy, sent for our destruction. Tell us where he lurks or it will be the worse for you.'

'If you really want to find him,' replied the ancient man, 'turn up this crooked way to yonder grove. I left him there to-day under an old oak-tree, and he is waiting still. He is not hard to find. God save you and amend your ways.'

And with that, he left them. The revellers hastened with all speed up to the hoary oak, and there, among its roots, lay a glittering pile of golden coins. At the sight of them,

our revellers forgot their search for Death and fell to dis-
cussing what they should do next.

'We cannot carry them off by day,' said the most wicked
of the three, 'for then other folks will say that we are thieves
and we shall lose our find. No, let us draw lots, and he who
draws the longest shall go into the town for bread and wine.
We can pass the day merrily enough with these, and re-
move the gold by night.'

He cut three straws and hid them in his hand, and by his
contrivance the lot fell to the youngest, who set off at once
for the town.

As soon as he was out of sight, the first reveller said:

'Now you know, don't you, that you can trust me in
everything. Our fellow is off to the town, and there lies the
gold, waiting to be divided into three—how much better if
it were but two!'

'How could this be,' asked the other, 'when our companion knows that it is here? What would we tell him?'

'Nothing,' said the first, and he laughed evilly. 'Is
it a bargain, then? Swear faith and I will tell you what
to do.'

'I will not betray you,' was the reply.

'Well then,' said the first, 'when he comes back, get up
and wrestle with him as in sport. Then I will stab him in
the back and you must stab him too. Thus shall we have
equal share in his death and the gold.'

Meanwhile, the youngest was running to the town, and
as he ran the bright coins danced before his eyes.

'If only they could all be mine,' he thought, and then,
'but why not? Yes, why not?'

As soon as he arrived, he went to the nearest apothecary.

[54]

'Have you anything for rats,' said he, 'ay, and for a polecat that has been among the hens.'

'To be sure,' replied the apothecary, 'I have a poison here so strong that it will kill anything alive, be the draught never so small.'

The other took the box of poison and went to the next street, where he borrowed three large bottles. When no one was looking, he put poison into two, keeping the third clean, as well he might, for it was to be his own. Then he had all three filled up with wine.

He hastened back to his two companions and the pile of gold, and there they killed him just as they had planned.

'Now for a drink,' said one, 'before we share the gold.'

He took up a bottle, drank deeply and passed it to his friend, who did the same, and neither knew that poison was their choice. But soon, very soon, they lay beside their murdered fellow, and the gold that winked and glittered in the sun. They had found Death.

How Ysengrin the Wolf
was taught to fish

How Ysengrin the Wolf was taught to fish

RENART THE FOX and Ysengrin the wolf went for a walk together one dark night. Renart walked in front, his friend behind. It was Christmastime, the clear sky bright with stars, and before them Renart saw a fish‑pond gleam, frozen so hard you could have danced on it. Nevertheless, the local villagers, who each night brought their cattle to the pond, had pierced the ice so that the beasts could drink. There was a bucket floating in the hole, and Renart sniffed around it. He wore a schem‑ ing look. Slyly he glanced at Ysengrin and said:

'Come closer, Sir, and see what we have here. Observe that swarm of swimmers through the hole. Mark this con‑ traption; with it we shall catch fat eels and suchlike, shoals of dainty fish.'

'Sir Renart,' said the other, taken in, 'catch me that object by its handle, pray, and tie it to my tail.'

Renart seized the bucket and bound it to the tail as best he could.

'Dear brother Ysengrin,' he said, 'move not an inch, I beg. The fish will come at any minute now.'

He lay underneath a bush, placed his nose upon his paws, and hoped for diverting things to come.

Ysengrin sat waiting on the ice. First, the bucket filled with icicles; the water in the hole began to freeze; the floes around the bucket packed in tight; the tail was sealed up with it in the ice. Ysengrin attempted to sit up and pull the bucket to him with its load. He thought that he had fish inside his pail! He tried in every way he could. In vain! The anguish from his trapped tail stabbed him through. He made a pitiful appeal:

How Ysengrin the Wolf was taught to fish

'Renart, my friend, I can no longer stay. See where the dawn is breaking in the east.'

The other, at his wails, raised up his head, opened his eyes, and watched him craftily.

'Sir,' he said, 'our business is complete. Now come away, my dearest friend, you have caught fish enough.'

The voice of Ysengrin went up a tone:

'Renart,' he howled, 'there are too many here. I cannot lift them out—we have caught more than any man can tell.'

The fox replied: 'He loses all, who covets all'—and grinned.

The dark night passes and the clear dawn breaks; the sun of morning rises up on high to shine on paths made white by drifting snow. And with the sun, Messire Constant des Granges, whose house adjoined the pool, sprang out of bed. He seized a horn and shouted for his dogs, ordered his hunter to be saddled up, put the whole household in a great to-do. Renart, at this tumult, ran away, off to his den, and dug himself in deep.

But Ysengrin remained, caught in the trap. He toiled and laboured, shook himself and pulled, so hard that he near ripped off his whole hide. Had he to lose the half of his poor tail to free it from the ice? While he strained his muscles there appeared a servant running that way, with some hare-hounds on a leash. He spotted Ysengrin, thought for a moment, yelled:

'Aha! the wolf! Aha! Aha!' and hearing this, the hunters sallied forth each vying with the next to jump the fence. The wolf's distress increased. For close behind, came Constant at full gallop on his horse. He shouted as he slithered down the slope:

[60]

How Ysengrin the Wolf was taught to fish

'Let go the dogs! Dogs forward straightaway!'
The hounds, uncoupled, fastened on the wolf. The
hackles rose on our friend, Ysengrin. The huntsmen egged
the dogs on savagely, and their poor prey, hard pressed,
snapped at their heads. He bit and bit. What else, pray,
could he do? He would have preferred peace, without a
doubt. Constant unsheathed his sword to strike a blow. He
got down from his horse and joined the wolf upon the ice,
intending to attack him from behind. He swung. He
missed. The blow went skimming past the spine of Ysengrin and his dread foe fell flat upon his back. Up on his
feet once more with difficulty, Sir Constant bore down on
the hapless wolf. Hark to the battle proud that there befell!
He aimed at our friend's head and took a swipe. The
blade went sliding down towards the tail and took it clean
off just above the ice. Ysengrin waited for no more. He
bounded to one side to get away, but the wretched hounds
redoubled their attack, hanging by their teeth about his
flanks. He left them as a fee his lovely tail which cost so
much. A little longer and his heart would break—how
could he get away? He found that he was equal to the task.
There was a mound behind, guarding his back, and
though the attacks in front were multiplied, he fended them
all off and did not flag. At last the hounds gave way, drew
back and gave him up. He promptly fled and buried himself deep in some far wood. And gasping there, he swore
he'd be revenged on Renart the next time they chanced to
meet.

[61]

Sir Gawain and the Green Knight

KING ARTHUR was at Camelot for the
Christmas feast with many noble lords and
gallant knights, and all the loveliest ladies
in the land. The festival was held for fifteen
days, with music and merriment by day,
dancing by night, until New Year came
round. The company assembled in the hall to give their
New Year's gifts and then to dine, the King at his High
Table with the Queen and his nephews Gawain and
Aggravain. Now Arthur had a custom not to eat on such
a festival before someone had told a wondrous tale of high
adventure or had challenged him to combat, in the joust to
lay life for life in jeopardy. In came the first course, heralded
by trumpets; all the many dishes, the beer and the wine,
were set before the company, save for the King alone. But
scarcely was this first course served and the noise abated,
when in at the hall-door there haled such a man as none in
that company had ever seen before. Though certainly a
man, he was so tall, so large of limb, of body so immense,
that he must have been half-giant at the least. Yet he was
well-proportioned, fair indeed, in all respects save one—he
was bright green. Every garment that he wore, his tunic,
mantle, hood and hose, albeit silken, set with precious
stones, embroidered all with birds and butterflies, was of
the same hue, saving his gold spurs. He rode a giant horse,
as green as grass, his tail and forelock tied with emerald
bands, studded with gems and little golden bells. The
horse's long, thick mane, combed, crisped and plaited with
gold filigree, was not longer than his master's shaggy hair,
which, mingling with his beard, hung round him to the
elbow like a cape. This stranger bore no hauberk, spear or

shield, but in one hand he held a holly bob, most green when all the wintry groves are bare, and in the other an enormous axe. Its spike was of green steel and hammered gold, its blade bright burnished and its edge as sharp as any razor. He rode straight to the dais, greeting none, but look, ing high above the tallest heads. The first words that he spoke were rough and rude:

'Where is the master of this company? I wish to see him and to speak with him.'

He ran his eye along the rows of knights as if to pick out the most prominent, and quite ignoring Arthur where he sat. They all stood silent. Every gallant knight had wit, nessed many marvels on his quests but never such as this. For fear of phantoms and the fairy-kind, no one dare reply, till Arthur broke the silence with these words:

'Fellow, be welcome here. I am the lord, and Arthur is my name. Sit down, I pray you, stay, and we will serve whatever you desire.'

'It was not my intent,' the other said, 'to tarry here at all. But your fame, my lord, is great, your castles deemed the best, and courtesy well known in this your court. All these things bring me hither at this time. That I come in peace and seek no strife, you may see from this holly-branch I bear. If I had wanted now to fight with you, I have a hauberk and a helm at home, a shield and a bright spear. I want no war—hence is my garb more soft. If you are bold as all men say, you will grant the game that I demand.'

'Courteous knight,' said Arthur, 'if you crave a fight you shall not lack it long.'

'I crave no combats—on this bench are naught but beardless boys. No man to match me here! So in this court

[65]

I beg a Christmas game, for it is Yule and also New Year's Day. If any here now holds himself so bold that one stroke for another he dare strike, I shall give him as a New Year's gift, my axe, and I shall bear his first blow though unarmed. But you must grant me, Arthur, the full right to pay him back with such another stroke, a twelvemonth and a day from this New Year.'

If they were at first astonished, even more so were they now, the high and the low who sat in Arthur's hall. The troll turned in his saddle, rolled his eyes, and bent his brows, as, wagging his rough beard, he watched to see who then would rise. When no one made a stir, he coughed aloud and proudly preened himself:

'What! Is this Arthur's house, that all the fame runs of, through many realms? Where is now your pride and sur-quidry, where your fierceness and your mighty words? The fame of the Round Table is cast down with one word of a single stranger's speech!'

At this, he laughed so loud that Arthur blushed for shame and, rising, said:

'Folly you ask and folly you shall get! No one is afraid of your big words! Give me now your axe and *I* shall play this New Year's game with you.'

Lightly he ran to him and caught his hand; fiercely the other sprang down off his horse. Arthur had the axe and swung it high, thinking to strike; the other stroked his beard with face unmoved, smoothed down his coat and was no more dismayed at the impending blow than if a man had brought him wine to drink. Before it fell, Sir Gawain leaned across to where they stood, and said:

'Lord, I beseech you! This combat must be mine! Bid me

come down to you, that I may leave my place without dis-
courtesy to your fair Queen. It is not seemly, Lord, that you
should take this challenge up yourself, while bold men sit.
I am the weakest here, feeblest of wit, and so the loss of my
life will be least. Since I have asked it first, grant me the
game.'

They whispered to each other, then the King, that
Gawain be allowed to take his place, so Arthur bade the
knight come to the floor and placed the axe in his young
nephew's hands. The Green Knight said:

'Now tell me true, fair sir, what you are called, before we
start our game.'

'Gawain I am called, who give this blow, and promise,
this time twelvemonth, to receive another with what weapon
you may choose.'

'Sir Gawain,' said the Green Knight, 'I am pleased that
you are the one to give the blow I ask. You have rehearsed
the covenant I made without a fault, but you must promise,
too, to seek me out alone wherever I may be, to receive such
wages as you deal.'

'Where shall I find you? Where is the place you live?'
asked Gawain. 'I do not know your home, nor yet your
court, nor even your true name. Pray tell me these and I
shall do my best.'

'No more is needed on this New Year's Day than to tell
you home and name when you have struck. The better for
you if I waste no more words, for you can stay here in your
Uncle's court until the time, and look no further hence.
Take up your grim tool now, and let us see how you can
smite.'

'Gladly,' said Gawain, and stroked the fearful axe. The

Green Knight bent his head and bared his neck, pulling his long locks forward from the crown. Gawain set his left foot to the ground before him, swung the axe, and let it fall so that the sharp blade cut sheer through the bones and out the other side. The edge of burnished steel bit in the ground; the handsome head went rolling down the floor, spurned from foot to foot, while from the trunk the hot blood sprang and shone bright on the green. The fellow did not falter for all that, but marched forth stoutly and reached out to where the men stood, catching up his head. He went to his steed and seized it by the reins, set one foot in the stirrup and swung the other up, sitting in the saddle as if nothing ailed him, headless though he were. He held the head up high and turned its face toward the King, and Gawain who was standing at his side. Then its eyes flew open and it looked at them full broad. Its mouth said:

'Gawain, you must see to it that you fulfil the promise that you made. I charge you to receive just such a blow as you have dealt me here, paid promptly on the first day of next year. As the Knight of the Green Chapel am I known both near and far. Fail not to come, or else be recreant.'

His head held in his hands, he jerked the reins and galloped out of Arthur's hall so fast that the green steed's hooves struck fire from the flint.

Sir Gawain and the King began to laugh. Though Arthur was amazed, he showed no sign, but courteously he turned toward the Queen:

'Do not be frightened, Lady Guinevere. Such an event well suits the Christmastide. Now I can turn to feasting with good heart, for I have seen a wonder in this hall.' He glanced at Gawain:

[68]

'Sir, hang up your axe!' he said, 'for you have hewn enough.' They hung it high for everyone to see, as witness to the truth of this strange tale. Then they sat down to the feast again and spent the day in mirth and revelry.

Thus Yuletide passed. The seasons came around in their due order until all too soon the feast of Michaelmas arrived again and made Sir Gawain think of New Year. He stayed with Arthur to Allhallow's Day. A feast was held then for the young knight's sake, and though the lords and ladies grieved for him, they jested joyessly to clear his heart. After the food he went up to the King:

'Now, my liege lord, I must ask your leave tomorrow to set out upon my quest.' He made good cheer, for there seemed no escape from what was destined. Early the next morning he was armed from head to foot in shining golden mail and mounted Gringolet his faithful steed. Lastly he set on his jewelled helm and slung the red shield with its gold device upon a silken baldric at his back. Now he was ready, and bade them all farewell, for evermore, as he and they believed.

Through the realm of Logres Gawain rode, sick at heart and fearful for his life. Sometimes he found a lodging for the night with kindly folk, at other times he slept under the sky. None but his horse had he for company along the way, no one to talk to on the road save God. He travelled on until he reached North Wales and the wilderness of Wirral, all the time asking as he went, if anyone had heard of a green knight, or a green chapel anywhere about. But all that he encountered said that never in their lives had they seen such a man or such a place. By perilous paths he roamed, climbed cliffs in countries strange, and at every ford he came to there stood a foe to fight. Dragons he slew and wolves, bulls and bears and boars, wild men that lived in crags, and monstrous trolls that panted after him among the fells. They would have killed him had he been less brave, and yet the winter troubled him far more than any of his divers enemies. Cold, clear water was spilling from the clouds and freezing before ever it reached earth. He slept in his irons more nights than enough in the naked rocks, where cold burns ran clattering from the crests, and froze in icicles.

On the morning before Christmas he arrived in a wood with high hills on every side. Great, hoary oaks were standing there, and gnarled hawthorns twined round with hazel trees. Everywhere trailed long festoons of moss. On the bare branches many a wretched bird piped piteously for pain of winter's cold. He was wondering in that wilderness where he might spend the night, when suddenly he saw, beyond the trees, a dwelling on a mound within a moat, set in a highfenced park—the fairest castle that a knight could own. He surveyed it as it shimmered through the oaks, then spurred Gringolet to the drawbridgeend. The bridge was up and all the gates shut fast, so Gawain sat and pondered on the bank, looking at the towers and battlements. So many painted pinnacles were scattered here and there, it seemed a castle cut from paper and not real. In answer to his call, a porter came, who greeted the knight errant courteously.

'Good sir,' said Gawain, 'will you tell your lord that I am seeking shelter for the night?'

'Yes,' said the porter, 'and I know you will be welcome for as long as you may wish.'

He went, but soon returned with many folk to bring the stranger in. They led him to the courtyard, took his steed, then brought Sir Gawain in to the warm hall. Many a lord pressed round to help the knight unarm and the master of the castle greeted him:

'Good sir, I bid you welcome. All I have is yours to use.'

He was getting on in years but a giant still in size, stout of limb and with a bushy beard. He led Gawain to a chamber where a fire was burning bright. The floor was carpeted, the walls were richly hung with tapestries, the bed had silken curtains running on great golden rings. The knight's old clothes were taken and fine robes were put upon him, then they sat him in a chair beside the fire. His spirits rose as he got warm. They fell to asking eagerly, who he was, from whence he came and why he passed that way. When their lord learned he was Gawain and from the court of Arthur, he laughed aloud and all his retinue rejoiced:

'Now we shall learn graciousness and courtly behaviour, for the courtesy of Gawain is widely renowned.'

After dining, they heard evensong, and as they left the chapel, Gawain saw the castle's lady, more fair than Guinevere! He hastened down the chancel to greet her and another—old, ugly and misshapen, but yet held in high esteem. They took him now between them and went to the lord's chamber, where they passed the evening merrily with wine before the fire.

The next day being Christmas, a feast was held with merriment, and while it lasted Gawain sat beside his host's fair wife. The music and dancing lasted three days fully, and on the third day Sir Gawain thanked his host who then replied:

[71]

'Mine is the honour, that Gawain has been with us!' He asked the knight what kept him from Camelot at Christ-mas, and learned then the whole story of the Green Knight and his blow.

'But I do not know,' said Gawain, 'where I am to find this chapel—can you tell me where it lies, I have but three days left.'

'Be at your ease,' the lord replied, 'it is but two days hence, so stay and after New Year's day you shall be shown the place.' Sir Gawain accepted this offer with great joy.

'You are weary from your journey,' said his host. 'Stay in your room and lie at ease the morning long, dine with my fair wife while I am away, for I shall hunt the hills at crack of dawn.' Gawain agreed to this. The other said: 'Let us strike this bargain too—whatever *I* catch shall be yours and whatever *you* get, give to me.' They sealed the bargain with a drink and so the night was passed.

The lord went to the forest before the sun was up, but Gawain lay abed until the light gleamed on the walls. He was woken by a little noise and peeping through the curtains he saw the lady enter. She sat down on the bed. The knight, surprised, had closed his eyes again.

'Good morrow,' said the lady, 'Sir, you are unwary to let someone, perhaps a foe, reach you before you wake. You are my prisoner, Gawain, and I shall not let you go.'

'Good morrow, lady,' Gawain said, 'I yield me to your grace. If you would grant me leave to rise and dress, I should be better able to converse.'

She would not let him go but professed undying

love. The astonished knight was then much put to it to answer her politely yet refuse to say that he too loved her in return.

'Can you be Gawain, flower of courtesy and best of knights?' the lady said. She stooped to kiss him, then went on her way. He quickly dressed and went to mass, then dined between the ladies, young and old, thankful for the old crone's company. When the lord came home, he brought a deer, which he gave to the knight:

'What think you of my prize?'

'It is the finest and best that I have seen in wintertime this seven year,' Sir Gawain said.

'And I give it to you,' his host replied, 'and thus fulfil our covenant.'

'By that same covenant I give you this,' said Gawain, 'It is all that I have won.' He kissed him on the cheek.

'It is good that you return it,' said the lord, 'but even better if you tell me whence it came.'

'That is outside our bargain,' Gawain said, and after that the matter rested.

The second day, before the cock crowed thrice, the lord went hunting up among the crags, and his wife came once again to Gawain's room. She mocked him for his lack of gallantry but he refused to be disloyal to his host. This time she kissed him twice, and kisses two he rendered to her husband in return for the monstrous boar that the lord brought home.

On the third day, the lord rose with the sun, in a frosty morning, for the hunt. The rocks around them echoed back the horns, and hounds bayed high and shrill in the cold air. The lady came a third time to the knight, and still Gawain

[73]

with courtesy refused to say he loved her. Kisses three she gave him as she left, and said:

'Pray give me some small thing, your glove perhaps, which may abate my grief when you are gone.'

'A glove is of too little worth to be a gift from Gawain; I have nothing with me I could give.'

'If I have nothing of yours,' the lady said, 'at least you shall accept a gift of *mine*.' She offered him a ring of pure red gold which bore a stone as shining as the sun.

'I have nothing to give, so will not take,' was all he said.

'If you refuse because it is too rich, then pray take this which seems of lesser worth.' She untied then the girdle of her gown. It was of green silk, all adorned with gold. She begged the knight to take it; he would not.

'Do you scorn it as a poor thing of itself? Then know its worth! Whoever wears this belt cannot be slain by any earthly stroke.'

Gawain looked at the girdle, and it came into his heart that such a gift might save his life in the combat of the next day. He was young and loved his life. He did not want to die. So he took the girdle, promising not to tell her lord. He paid only the three kisses for the fine fox's pelt which her husband brought him in the evening when he came. As they went to their beds, Sir Gawain said:

'May God repay you for your courtesy, my lord. But I pray you give me guidance to the chapel as you said. It is New Year's Day tomorrow when I needs must meet my fate.'

The weather grew colder as the long night passed, and snow was whirled by whistling winds, driven in drifts to fill the dales. Though Gawain closed his eyes he could not sleep and knew the hour by every cock that crowed. He dressed by lantern-light before the day, putting warm clothes underneath his mail. He called for Gringolet and mounted him. The drawbridge was lowered, all the gates unbarred, and with one servant he rode on his way. Cloud hung on the moor and melted on the mountains, each hill had a hat, a mantle of mist. Brooks boiled and burst their banks wherever they poured down and the high hill that they halted on was covered in white snow. There the man that had directed him bade him pause a moment:

'I have guided you this far, and the place you seek is near. But I shall tell you truthfully, since you are a man I honour, that the place you press on to, is deemed full perilous. In that wasteland dwells a creature, the mightiest in Middle-earth, bigger than the best four of your uncle Arthur's court. There is no man so proud of arms who passes by the chapel, that he does not challenge straight away, for he is merciless, be it churl or chaplain, monk or mass-priest even. Had you *twenty* lives and came there, you would surely lose them all. So turn some other way. I will tell no one what happened.'

'I think you wish me well, but if I left this place I would be a craven knight that might not be excused. I must go to the Green Chapel and abide what may befall.'

'I will ride with you no further. Take your helmet and your spear. Go down this slope until you reach the bottom of the dale. You will see the chapel and its guard to your left hand. Farewell, my lord. Go in God's name. I would not further bear you fellowship for all the gold on earth!' With that, he turned his horse and rode away.

Sir Gawain spurred forward, down into the valley. A wilderness it seemed without a sign of life, only high, steep

[75]

banks and jagged rocks all round. Nothing like a chapel could the knight see anywhere, but suddenly he came upon a mound, a sort of hill or hummock by the stream. He dismounted from his horse and looped the reins over a branch, then walked around, debating what it was. It had a hole at either end, on either side as well, and was overgrown with grasses and rank weeds. It was hollow inside and as far as he could tell, was nothing but a crevice in a crag.

'Can this be the Green Chapel?' said the puzzled knight. 'Well might the devil matins sing at midnight in this place. Ugly and quite overgrown with weeds—fit place indeed for that troll clad in green!'

Spear in hand, he walked up to the rock, then heard from the high bank beyond the brook a fearsome noise. Thwack! it clattered on the cliff as though to cleave the rock in two. It sounded as if someone were whetting a great scythe. Thwack! it was whirring like water in a mill. Thwack! it was ringing out terrible to hear.

'By God!' said Gawain then, 'is this a greeting meant for me? Who is there here to meet me, for Gawain is passing by! If anyone wants anything, let him come now or never!'

'Wait!' said someone on the bank, 'you shall have all I promised.' Yet he went on with that whirring sound, and disappeared, still whetting, as if he would come down. He appeared out of a hole, whirling his dire weapon—a huge axe, newly sharpened to deal the promised stroke. From top to toe he was in green, just as before, but this time walked, and when he reached the water, would not wade but leaped lightly over leaning on his axe.

'Gawain, you are welcome! You know the covenant between us. There is no one here to part us and none but

us to know. Take your helmet from your head and prepare
to have your pay.'

'Strike your stroke,' said Gawain, 'I shall not stir, nor
tremble.' He bared his neck, the axe swung high and would
have been his death, but he glimpsed the blade come glid-
ing and shrank back just a little, for fear of the sharp edge.
The other stayed his hand and then reproached the prince:

'You are not Gawain the valiant, who never was afraid!
I neither flinched nor fled in the court of good King
Arthur, though my head rolled to my feet—and *you* shrink
without a touch! Maiden and not man you were better to
be called.'

'I flinched once, but not again,' Sir Gawain said, 'and
yet if *my* head falls upon the floor I cannot put it back!
Hurry, man, and I shall bear your stroke without a start.
You have my word.'

'Have at thee then,' the other said and raised the axe aloft.
But yet again he stayed his hand before the blade could bite,
though Gawain not a finger stirred but stood as still as
stone, or a stock deep-rooted in the earth. The green man
said: 'So! Then you are whole of heart again! Now in
earnest can I strike my blow.'

'Strike on then,' said Gawain, 'you have talked too much
already.' A third time the axe swung high but did no more
than nick the flesh on one side of his neck. When Gawain
saw the blood gleam on the snow, he sprang back fast and
drew his shining sword.

'The debt is paid!' he cried, 'if you strike more than just
this one, I shall requite your blows.'

The troll drew back, and leaned upon his axe, shaft to
the ground, his elbow on the blade. At heart he was well

pleased with this young knight. He watched him as he stood there unafraid, then said:

'Brave knight, be not so stormy! I offer no more strokes. You have fulfilled the covenant we made. If I had so desired I could have done you hurt, but I tricked you twice with feints for the kisses that you got and yet paid back most truly as we had agreed. But the third time you deceived me and from this came your wounding—for the girdle that you wear is mine and woven by my wife. I sent her to assay you, but she found you faultless, save that you lacked in loyalty because you loved your life.'

'A curse on your trickery, for fear of you brought coward/ ice. Now am I false who have always shunned treachery and lies.'

'I account it as nothing, you have confessed so cleanly. I give you, Sir, this girdle, as green as my garments, as a token of the truth of our encounter here. But come back to my castle for the rest of this high festival.'

'I am too ashamed,' said Gawain, picking up his helmet. 'Commend me to your ladies who have me thus beguiled, the young one and the old. But the girdle I will take. To remind me of my shame I shall look upon it often and when pride of prowess comes upon me, one glance my heart will humble. Pray tell me now your rightful name, since you rule this land.'

'Bercilak de Hautdesert am I called in this country. The ancient lady in my house is Morgan le Fay. She it was who forced me to make trial of you thus. She wanted to kill Guinevere with fright at the green giant, standing at her table with his head held in his hand. But come and feast with us, she will cause no further mischief.'

[78]

'I must be gone,' said Gawain, and took his leave most courteously. Wild ways he rode on Gringolet, yet came to court at last. There was joy in Arthur's hall when they saw the knight returning. He showed them the green girdle, and told them all the tale.

'It is the token of the untruth I was taken in,' said Gawain, 'I will wear it forever to remind me of my shame.'

But all the lords laughed loudly and vowed to wear girdles in honour of Sir Gawain, and his quest of the Green Knight.

The Alchemist

Chaucer

The Alchemist

THERE WAS ONCE a London chantry-priest who was a greedy, avaricious man. One day, a certain canon came to him and asked him for a small loan for three days. 'I'll pay you on the nail,' the canon said, 'upon my honour as a man of God.'

And sure enough, on the appointed day, back came the canon with the sum in full. The chantry-priest was very much impressed:

'I don't mind lending to an honest man who pays back all his debts, and promptly too. Men like you are few and far between.'

'As if I would not pay!' the canon cried. 'However could you think of such a thing? I, who prize honour far above all else! But come, since you have shown yourself a friend, I'll tell you something that will make you rich. I'll work a very miracle for you!'

'Oh, can you really?' asked the eager priest, who was both a miser and a fool.

'Just send your servant out for mercury and you will see,' the canon then replied.

The servant was dispatched and soon returned with several ounces of the shining stuff. The canon laid them out most carefully, then sent the servant off to fetch some coal, and when this had been done, he fished about and from his clothes produced a crucible. He measured out an ounce of mercury and poured it in, saying as he did:

'This powder of my own invention makes pure silver out of simple mercury. Send your servant out and lock the door. We don't want him to spy on what we do.' The servant was dismissed, the fire was lit, the powder dropped

inside the crucible, which then they covered up with burn-ing coals.

'So that you can see there are no tricks,' the canon said, 'I'll leave it all to you.'

And while the priest was busy at the fire, adding more coals and fanning up the flame, the canon got a bit of beechwood out, charred to a coal and with a hole bored in, where he had poured an ounce of silver dust then stopped the hole with wax to keep it in. While the priest was poking at the fire, his back to what was happening in the room, the canon palmed the beechwood and then said:

'Oh, not like that! Give me the poker here. You're get-ting hot—you'd better wipe your face.'

He gave the priest a cloth and as he wiped he could not see the canon at the fire placing the beechwood on the crucible.

'Let's have a drink!' the cheerful canon cried. 'We'll take a rest now, till the thing is done.'

The wax inside the beechwood melted fast and let the silver fall, as he had planned, into the crucible. After a time, the canon rose and said:

'We haven't any chalk to make a mould. You must buy some, but I'll come with you, so that you won't think I'm cheating you.'

When they got back, the canon took the chalk and, giv-ing the witless priest some other task, he slipped a silver rod out of his sleeve, cut the chalk to fit, then popped it back. They took the preparation from the fire, poured it in the mould and then set this inside a pan of water to cool down.

'Look what we've got!' the canon cried, and there on the water floated silver dust. When the priest reached down into

[84]

the mould his fingers met upon the silver rod, which the canon had that minute slipped inside.

'A miracle, a miracle! Oh, teach me how it's done. I can be rich then in no time at all,' pleaded the foolish priest. He did not wonder why, if the canon held the key to wealth without an end, he had asked a loan of *him*.

'Well, first of all, we'll have another go, just to show you there's no knavery and that I can do it every time,' the canon said. Then he performed his 'miracle' again. This time, he stirred the mixture with a stick, and in this stick an ounce of silver dust had been stuffed earlier and sealed in tight with wax. The wax dissolved, the silver dropped, and floated on the water in the pan when the mould was cooled. And when the priest went fishing in the bowl, he came up with a second silver rod.

'Do you think you see how it is done?' the canon asked. 'Practice makes perfect. Let's do it just once more. But this time we'll use copper and you'll see that we shall get the very same result.'

So once again, the experiment was tried, and when the molten copper in the mould had cooled into a rod, the canon switched it for a silver one, by sleight of hand, pretending all the while that though he groped, he could find nothing there.

'Help me, Sir Priest,' he said, 'help me to get it out.'

The priest rolled up his sleeve, dipped in his hand, and straightway came upon the silver rod. His wonder knew no bounds.

'We must take these rods,' the canon said, 'to a silver-smith in this vicinity, and ask him if he thinks our silver real, or just some worthless alloy we have made.'

They did so, and the silversmith pronounced the three rods to be silver, as they were, and bought from his own shop the day before!

'Oh, will you sell your recipe to me,' the priest beseeched, 'so that *I* can make this powder too, that can work such wondrous miracles.'

'It will be rather dear,' the canon said. 'How much can you afford? Apart from me, there's but a single friar who knows the secret of my recipe. I'll tell you what, because you are a friend and once helped me, I'll let you have it for just forty pounds, and cheap too, at the price.'

With that, the priest went hurrying round his friends and raked up forty pounds in golden coins to buy the canon's 'miracle'. I need not tell you that, hard as he tried, he never made a single silver rod, nor that the canon and his forty pounds were never seen in London Town again.

The Two Lovers

The Two Lovers

THERE IS A MOUNTAIN-PEAK in Nor-
mandy which towers to the sky, and at its
feet, a little to one side, the town of Pître
stands. There was a king of Pître, long ago,
who had one child, a daughter sweet and
fair on whom, since his young wife, her
mother, died, he lavished all his love. His subjects wished
the Princess to be wed; her father could not bear to part
with her. So at last, he hit upon a plan whereby they could
not say he held her back, yet she could not be won. He
would let her marry, so he said, but first her suitors had to
pass a test. Each must bear her to the very top of the high
mountain just outside the town. If he set her down upon the
way, he failed. So many tried, so many went away, dis-
comfited! For though the maid was light, the peak was
high. It looked as if she never would be wed.

But at her father's court there was a man, the young son
of a count, both fair of face and courteous of mien, whose
heart was set on being a great knight. He loved the Princess,
and she loved him back, but no one knew except those two
alone, so secret were they, fearing the King's wrath. Tiring
of this secrecy at last, he asked her to elope. It seemed the
only way for them to wed, for if he asked her father for her
hand, he would have to face the mountain-test which all
had failed. But she would not agree.

'I will not cause my father such great grief because I love
him dearly,' said the maid. 'There is a way that you can pass
the test. Go now to Salerno, to my Aunt, and ask her help.
Tell her how things stand. She is famous for her skill with
plants and herbs, and may have some philtre that will give
you strength to win.'

The Two Lovers

The young man hurried home and packed his bags, then post-haste to Salerno off he went. The aunt, when she had heard his sorry tale, agreed to help him. Giving him a phial, she then said:

'When you drink this philtre you will feel no tiredness from any weight you bear.'

He reached the court, and went straight to the King. He asked him for the hand of the Princess. The King was sure that he would fail the test—someone so young could hardly hope to win where older, stronger men had met defeat. The strongest of them only reached half-way! And so he let him try. All the vassals of the King from far and near were summoned there to witness the attempt. They gathered in a meadow near the Seine on the appointed day. The maiden came, clad only in her shift—her gorgeous robes, encrusted thick with gems, she left behind, for these would be an added weight to bear. She had each day been eating less and less to help her love succeed in his hard task. He thought that nothing could destroy their hopes as they set off, she carrying the phial, he bearing her. When they were half-way up, the Princess said:

'Please drink the philtre here. Your strength will fail.'

But he replied:

'My heart is very strong. I will not drink as long as I can climb yet three more steps. Beside, those down below will see if we stop now.'

So on he went.

Two thirds of the way up to the top, further than any man had gone before, he stumbled, almost dropped her.

'Drink the philtre,' his love begged him, but in vain. He did not even seem to hear her speak. He was too proud to use the philtre's strength and on he toiled. He staggered to the top and set her down, then fell exhausted, and lay very still. She kneeled beside him, begging him to drink and use the philtre now that he had won. He did not answer. He would never speak. His heart had burst within his labouring breast. She hurled the philtre down and to this day, strong herbs have grown and flourished where it fell. The maiden lay beside him in her grief, and wept there on the ground till her heart broke.

The people waiting for them grew alarmed when they did not return, and came to see what could have happened there. How great their grief was when they learned the truth! The sad king had a marble coffin made and buried them together on the peak. That mountain outside Pître is still called 'Les Deux Amants' after that sad pair.

The Three Plagues of Britain

The Three Plagues of Britain

THERE WAS A KING in the old, old days, whose name was Ludd. He it was who built London's walls and raised higher towers on them, then gave the town his name. His brother was Llefelys, a wise man, who married the heiress to the throne of France and thus became the king. All went well in their two realms for a time, but then in Britain three dire plagues befell. The first was the arrival of a race called the Coranieid. Not a thing was said, or whispered even, in all Britain that they did not hear, borne along the wind. The second plague was a most fearful scream, that sounded by every hearth on each May-Eve. Strong men grew pale, the women swooned away and all the earth grew barren at that cry. The third thing that befell was that the food prepared in the King's courts would never last beyond a single night even if they fetched a year's supply. King Ludd was much grieved since he did not know how he could rid the island of these plagues. By the counsel of his nobles, he set sail at last for France, to ask his brother Llefelys for help. They put out to sea in secret, but Llefelys heard the news and sailed against them with his fleet, not knowing why they came, whether for peace or war. They met in the mid-Channel, and the flagships of each side sailed to each other and the two kings met. They wondered how they might discuss these plagues without the Coranieid hearing them. Then Llefelys had a bronze horn made. If they spoke through this, he told King Ludd, the wind could not now bear their words away. But their speech was strangely muddled when it travelled through the horn, and King Llefelys guessed there was a demon down inside. So he

[94]

poured wine in to wash the demon out, and after that their words were clear and plain. King Llefelys said that he would give some insects to his brother.

'Keep a few,' he said, 'and breed some more in case the plague returns, but mash the rest in water and then call your whole realm to one place. You must cast the water on their heads—your Britons will not come to any harm, but the Coranieids will all die.

'The second plague,' Llefelys said, 'the scream by your hearthside, is caused by the native dragon of your land. A foreign dragon is attacking him and so he screams. You must measure Britain, length and width as well, and in the exact middle dig a pit. Place at the bottom a large vat of mead and cover it over with a silken sheet. You will see the dragons' battle rage and they will fight in many monstrous shapes. At last they will grow weary and fall down in the shape of little pigs upon the silk. They will sink down on it and drink the mead. Then while they sleep, wrap them in the sheet and bury them in a coffin made of stone in the strongest place in all your realm. As long as they are there, no other plague will fall upon the land.

'As for the third thing troubling you,' he said, 'there is a great enchanter who each time you lay up store of food and costly wines, makes all your household sleep so he can steal. You must yourself keep vigil at your feasts and stand a tub of water near at hand—step in it every time you feel sleep come.'

So Ludd went back to Britain and there called a great assembly. Just as his brother said, he mashed the insects and sprinkled everyone. All the Coranieid were destroyed but not a single Briton came to harm. Then Ludd had Britain

[96]

measured, length and breadth, and found in Oxford its exact mid-point. He had a pit dug there and in it put a vat of mead covered up with silk. He kept watch there all night and sure enough saw the two dragons fighting, till they sank into the vat, drank all the mead and then fell fast asleep. While they slept, Ludd wrapped them in the silk, and buried them in a coffin made of stone in the deepest part of all the land. After that the scream was heard no more.

Soon King Ludd gave orders for a feast and had a tub of water set by him just as Llefelys said. At about the third watch of the night everyone grew drowsy and they slept, save for the King who kept himself awake by standing in the water in the tub. At last he saw a man of monstrous size, and fully armed, come stealing to the hall. He had a basket into which he put all the food and wine they had prepared. The King leaped up at that and shouted out:

'Stop, stranger! You shall do us no more wrong unless you prove the stronger when we fight.'

The giant stood the basket on the ground and they fought long and hard, until he fell. Before King Ludd could kill him he cried out:

'I ask for quarter.'

'How can I grant that?' King Ludd then asked, 'after all the harm that you have done.'

'I will make good to you each loss I caused, and be your liegeman while my life shall last.'

The King accepted that, and thus it was that Ludd and Llefelys rid Britain of the plagues.

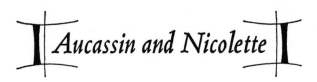

Aucassin and Nicolette

French Romance

ONCE, in Provence, there lived a noble count called Garin, who for many years waged war upon the fierce Count of Valence, his mortal foe. The story says that his castle, Biaucaire, was long besieged but Garin was himself too old and frail to lead his men to battle. He had one son, a youth named Aucassin, and Garin looked to him to lead his troops. But he would not. Instead he sat and sang and sighed, because his heart was given to a fair slave-girl, Nicolette, and he could think of nothing else but her. In vain his father begged that he should fight, for always he refused.

'Give me the slave-girl for my wife, and I will fight,' he said, but his father would have none of it.

'You will be Count of Biaucaire,' he cried, 'and fit match for the daughter of a king! She is a slave-girl captured in some war and fostered by the Captain of this town. You shall not marry her.'

So Aucassin stayed brooding in his room, and the siege continued. Then Count Garin thought:

'If I kill this wretched slave, or have her sent away, my son will soon forget her and bethink him of the war.'

So he sent then for the Captain of the town and said:

'That slave you captured from the Saracens and brought here as your child—send her away or else you both shall burn.'

The Captain went back to his home in fear. It was a stately mansion, fine and large, with many a rich room, to match his wealth, and since he could not find it in his heart to send the girl away, he had her locked up safe in one of these, with only an old crone for company, bidding her, if she wished to live, never to escape.

The tale that she had vanished ran throughout the town until at last it came to Aucassin. He hurried to the Captain of the town and asked if this were so.

'My Lord,' the Captain said, 'I fear you cannot see my Nicolette again, because your father threatens her with death.'

'I am grieved that it is so,' said Aucassin, and in deep sorrow went away.

Meanwhile, a fresh attack was being made on the beleaguered town. Count Garin went to his son's room and said:

'Aucassin, you must fight, or else we shall all perish.'

'Then grant me Nicolette to be my wife,' begged Aucassin.

'I would die first,' his father said.

'Then grant me but three words and just one kiss, and I will fight,' said Aucassin.

'That will I gladly do!' Count Garin cried.

So Aucassin was armed and horsed, and rode out of the city-gates, leading the Count's host, but still his thoughts were all on Nicolette and he struck not one blow, but was buffeted and beaten till he fell and was made prisoner. Then suddenly he thought:

'I am a prisoner now and soon I shall be dead. What good will be my father's promise then?'

Coming to himself, he drew his sword and smote to left and right. He cut his way straight through his father's foes until he reached the Count of fair Valence and captured him. The Count's supporters fled and he himself was

made to kneel down at Count Garin's feet to hear his judgement.

'Father, I claim the promises you made,' said Aucassin.

'What promises were those?' his father asked, pretending
that he did not understand.

'That I should have three words and just one kiss from
my true love, the slave-girl Nicolette,'

'That was in jest,' Count Garin mocked, 'to get you to
the war.'

Then indeed was Aucassin enraged:

'Sir, you have played me false! As you deny me my reward, so I deny your triumph.' And turning to his prisoner
he said:

'Most noble Count, if you will but swear never to harm
my father's land again you shall go free. We will not take
your life.'

The Count of Valence swore and was allowed to go his
way, for all Count Garin's cursing. In his rage, he ordered
that his son be flung into the deepest dungeon which the
castle owned.

And there must we leave Aucassin to turn to Nicolette.
It was the month of May, when in Provence the days were
warm and long, the nights serene and still. One night as
she was lying on her bed, she saw the bright moon through
the casement shine and from the garden heard a nightingale.
Everything seemed so peaceful and so fair until she thought
of old Count Garin's threat:

'There is no safety for me here, I know, while I still live.
I must escape.'

The old woman was asleep who guarded her, and so,

unseen, she tied her sheets together in a rope and, with it knotted to the window-frame, she slid into the garden down below. The dew was lying thick upon the grass so she lifted her long robe clear of the ground and ran swiftly to the garden-gate, keeping always to the shadowed side because the moonlight was as bright as day. Once through, she made her way down silent streets until, by chance, she reached the very tower above the dungeon where Aucassin lay. Its buttresses cast shadows all around and so she hid among them for a while, trying to think what it were best to do. As she sat there, her back against the wall, she heard Aucassin's voice from the dungeon down below, lamenting his sad fate. She now wept bitterly because she knew herself to be the reason for his plight and then she cut off her long hair and cast it through the window of the dungeon where he was, saying:

'By this remember me, for I must go into a far country or your father in his rage will kill both you and me.'

Aucassin called to her and begged her not to go. But, as he did, the watchman on the tower (who overheard each word the pair had said because the night air was so quiet and still) caught sight of soldiers coming down the street. Their swords were ready underneath their cloaks for the Count had ordered them to kill the girl, whose loss had been made known. The watchman pitied her so gave her word, and Nicolette shrank back against the wall until the soldiers had passed by, then swiftly fled.

When at last she reached the city-wall, she climbed it easily for in the war it had been broken and not mended here and there, but on the other side a deep fosse lay and she knew well that she would break her neck if once she slipped. Bravely she slid down the nearer side until she reached the bottom, cut and bruised, but if it had been hard once to get in, it would be even harder to get out! How was she to scale the other side, so smooth and sheer that even soldiers failed? By great good fortune she saw lying there a pike that fell in during the long siege, and with this she made rungs as she climbed up, until she gained the top.

Now, all before her, the vast forest lay. Thirty leagues it stretched, this way and that, filled with robbers and with ravening beasts, but the peril ahead seemed no more perilous than that which lay behind, so in she went. She crept into a thicket and slept there till late into the day.

It was the custom of the shepherds of the town to gather by a fountain in the woods to eat their midday meal. Now that the war was at an end and they could venture safely out of town, they came to their old haunt and while they ate their voices woke the sleeping Nicolette. When she saw not soldiers sitting there but humble shepherds, she thought she would be safe if she went up and asked them for their help.

'Fair sirs,' she said, 'pray tell me if you know of Aucassin, the son of our old Count.'

'Ay, to be sure,' said they, 'we know he lies in gaol!'

'Tell him there is a beast in this dark wood, to hunt it when he can. If he could capture it he would not give one limb of it for a hundred marks of gold, not for five hundred nor for any ransom.'

'There is no beast so great in all this land that a limb of it would fetch a single mark. You are some fairy-woman—off with you!'

[104]

'Do as I ask, I pray you. I will pay. Here are five golden coins and they are yours if only you will say to Aucassin that if he come to hunt within three days, he will be healed of all his present woes.'

'We cannot go to him, but if he pass then we will tell him.' And with that she had to rest content. She made her way into the forest-heart and built a little shelter there of boughs.

'If Aucassin should chance to pass this way, he will see the bower and guess that I am near. Then if he loves me truly he will wait.' Thus she reasoned as she broke the boughs and plaited them together as a roof. She hid in a coppice then to watch for him.

Meanwhile, the news of Nicolette's escape had reached Count Garin's ears. Thinking her by now out of his land, he had his son set free. He held a splendid feast, thinking to turn the young man's thoughts elsewhere, but while the courtiers laughed and danced and sang, Aucassin sat silent and withdrawn. Then an old knight gave him this advice:

'In my youth I languished out of love, the same as you,' he said, 'and in the forest found best remedy. A man forgets his sorrows in the hunt.' Aucassin thought over his advice, and next morning early he set out. At length he reached the fountain, just at noon, where the shepherds sat and ate their meal. They recognized him and their leader said:

'My lord, a maiden came to this same fountain yesterday at noon. She bade us tell you that there is a beast in this dark forest you must hunt.

'If you could capture it, you would not give one limb of

it for a hundred marks of gold, not for five hundred nor for any ransom.'

Aucassin knew that they meant Nicolette, and thanking them, he set off through the trees. He galloped with all speed through brake and briar, the brambles tore his clothes, his face was scratched by the low-hanging branches yet still he rode. Later that same night he reached the shelter Nicolette had made, and as the moon shone on its plaited boughs, was sure no hands but hers had woven it. He leaped down from his horse in such great haste he tripped on a large stone that lay nearby, and, falling, wrenched his shoulder out of joint. In pain he crept into the little bower, then lay there looking out at the bright stars. One of them seemed brighter than the rest and it reminded him of Nicolette. And as he thought of her, she came to him and bound his wounded shoulder with his shirt. Then they rode away into the night, rejoicing that at last they were both free.

But not for long, alas! Down upon the seashore the next day, they met the ship which was to carry them far from Count Garin's wrath, but they had scarce put out to sea before a fearful storm arose and drove them down the coast. They came to land at Torelore, a castle on a plain, and there received a welcome, to be sure, but shortly after this the castle was besieged, and fell into the hands of Saracens. All its inhabitants were carried off as slaves, and sorrow fell upon the luckless pair for they were parted once again. The ship which carried Aucassin was driven off its course by a gale which blew it back to Biaucaire, where it was wrecked. The Saracens were quickly thrown in chains and Aucassin set free amid great joy. Count Garin had just died of vexation, rage and grief, and so his son was made the rightful Count. The castle was now filled with revelry to celebrate Aucassin's safe return, but still his heart was sad. What cared he for wealth and rank if Nicolette were dead?

Unknown to him, however, Nicolette was safe aboard the fine and gallant ship which bore the King of Carthage and his sons, and that same wind which had wrecked Aucassin blew her to distant Africa. The King and his twelve sons honoured Nicolette; because she was so fair, they did not doubt that she was a lady of high lineage. But though they questioned her, still she could tell them nothing of herself for her first memory was of Biaucaire, till they got to Car' thage. Then, when she saw its gates and battlements, its soaring towers and lofty pinnacles, she knew it for her home. She knew she was the daughter of the King and sister to his sons. Softly to herself she sang of this, but the King of Carthage heard.

'What is it that you sing there, Nicolette?' he asked.

'That I am your daughter, Sire, and sister to your sons. It is fifteen years since last I saw your face. I was captured by your foes and sold in Biaucaire.'

The courtiers rejoiced when they heard this, knowing that their princess had returned, and the King led his daughter through the town to be restored to family and friends. Yet Nicolette was restless and grieved for Aucassin, because she did not know what had become of him. She wondered how she might get news of him and at last devised a clever plan. She got a viol for herself and learned to play, then left her father's palace one dark night, and went to a little cottage out of town, the home of her old nurse. There she changed her robes for a poor harper's clothes and stained her skin brown with the juice of herbs. In this guise she took ship for France, and travelled all the length of fair Provence, playing and singing, till she reached Biaucaire.

Thinking her a minstrel, the town-guards sent her to the castle to a feast, and there in the hall, unrecognized, she sang the tale of Nicolette and how she had reached Carthage where her father was the king. Aucassin sent for the harper straightaway.

'Is it true what you sing?' he asked her eagerly.

'It is,' the seeming minstrel then replied, 'I saw her in Carthage with the King. He wishes her to wed a Saracen, but she will have no lord save Aucassin.'

'Nor I a wife who is not Nicolette,' said Aucassin, 'so, harper, pray return from whence you came and bring her back to me.'

She bowed and took her leave, but not for distant Carthage as he thought. Instead she went down to her other home, the mansion of the Captain of the town. The Captain had just died, but his wife was overjoyed to see the foster-daughter she thought lost. The maiden took her rest there for eight days, and with the herb 'Eyebright' washed off the stain, leaving her skin white as it was before. When eight days had passed, the Captain's wife sent messages that Aucassin should come. The lady bearing them saw that he grieved because as yet his true love had not come.

'Grieve no more, my lord,' the lady said, 'but come with me and I will show to you the thing that you love best in all the world.'

And when he reached the mansion and his love, his

grief was banished and his heart made light. He married her next day, and with his bride lived happily for many years to come.

The Devil and the Summoner

Chaucer

The Devil and the Summoner

THERE WAS ONCE A SUMMONER who made a rich living by issuing false sum-monses. He would deliver the summons to his wretched victim, then let himself be bribed to get the charges dropped. One day he set off on just such a wicked errand, to visit a poor old widow who lived outside the town, and on his way through the streets he met a gay young fellow he had never seen before. Dressed in bright green he was, with a black-fringed hat and a stout long-bow slung at his back.

'Where might you be going?' asked the young stranger.

'Not far,' said the Summoner, much taken aback, 'just to fetch some rent that's owing to my lord.'

'Then you must be a bailiff,' the other said, and this was not denied, for the Summoner dared not say, for shame, what was his real trade.

'I am a bailiff too,' said the young fellow then, 'but I am a stranger in these parts. I should like to come with you as you go on your rounds, to learn the lie of the land, if you will allow it. In return, if you should ever come into my shire, I will promise to give you everything you need.'

To the Summoner this sounded like a chance for easy profit.

'It's a bargain,' he said quickly, and they rode off on their way.

Now the Summoner was a poking and prying sort of man, who made it his business to know everyone's affairs. So it was not long, as you might expect, before he began to question his new companion closely.

'Where do you live, then?' he presently enquired. 'I might decide to call on you at your house some day.'

'Oh, far away, up north,' replied the young man vaguely, 'I'll tell you where before we part—so well you'll never miss it. I hope to see you there sometime, yes indeed I do.'

The Summoner could see that he was getting nowhere so he changed the subject.

'Teach me the tricks of your trade,' he said, 'I'm always glad to benefit from other men's advice.'

'To tell you the truth,' said the young fellow then, 'I have a hard master who gives me small wages, so I'm forced to make a living by cheating and extortion. Even so, I only just contrive to make ends meet.'

'I couldn't make a living, I confess, if I were not prompt to take all that came my way. What a pair we make!' The Summoner laughed. 'We might as well swap names, now we know the rest.'

The other, all this time, had worn a little, secret smile.

'Do you really want to know my name?' he asked slyly. 'Well, I am a devil from Hell, and I thrive by taking any gift that's given. You have the same objective, wealth, no matter how acquired, save that you deal in money, I in souls. I am riding to the world's end, searching for my prey.'

'Well, I'll be damned,' exclaimed the Summoner, more truly than he knew. 'I took you for a man—you have a body just like me. Perhaps you wear another shape in Hell?'

'There is no need,' the fiend replied, 'of bodies where we dwell, for we can take on any shape at will, be it man or ape or angel even.'

'Why don't you stay one shape, why have so many?' the Summoner enquired.

'All the better to catch my prey if I appear the thing that

[114]

he knows best,' said the fiend, then fearing that he might have said too much and put the Summoner upon his guard, he went on hurriedly:

'Remind me to explain some time, when we've more leisure, but not now—we've done no business—you wouldn't understand in any case—I'm allowed to tempt men, by God's grace—come on now, we must hurry. I'll keep you company, unless you'd rather not.'

'That's all right by me,' the Summoner replied, 'we'll each take our own shares, but if one does better than the other, we'll split the extra profit.'

On they went, and at the entry to the widow's village, they met a farm-cart loaded high with hay and stuck fast in the mud. The carter was lashing his sweating team and swearing loudly:

'The Devil take you all,' he shouted, 'horses, cart *and* hay!'

'Go on,' whispered the Summoner, 'you heard what he said. Let's up and take the lot.'

'Ah, but you wait,' the fiend replied, 'you'll see he didn't mean it.' They watched the carter for a bit, as he laboured with his team, until at last he got the horses moving and the wheels spun clear of the mud.

'God bless you all, my beauties,' exclaimed the carter then, and——

'There, what did I tell you?' said the fiend. 'He said one thing perhaps, but what he meant is quite another tale. So let's be on our way.'

Now the Summoner broached his business in the village.

'There's an old widow living here,' he said, 'who would rather break her neck than lose a penny of her goods. I want twelve pence, or else she'll face the court, even if she *has* done no offence! You failed just now—I'll show you how it's done!'

By this time, they had arrived at the widow's gate and the Summoner went hammering at her door.

'Come out you wicked woman, you wretched miscreant!' he roared.

'Who's that a-knocking,' quavered the old dame, as she hobbled to the door, 'well, bless me, it's the Summoner— and what's your will?'

'On pain of excommunication, I hereby do summon you unto the court in town tomorrow, to defend yourself against those charges which shall be made against you.'

'Alas, alas!' shrieked the poor widow, 'but what am I to say? Oh, no, I couldn't make the journey at my age. Pray, Sir, write something down to save the trip, and let a lawyer answer in my stead.'

'All right, all right,' the Summoner then said, 'but you must pay at once. That's twelve pence, if you please. It's my master gets the profit and not I. Come on, I'm in a hurry to be gone.'

'Twelve pence!' exclaimed the widow, 'and where would I get that? You know I have not twelve pence in the world. Oh, Sir, show mercy and take pity on a poor old widow-woman such as I!'

'Cough up!' was all the Summoner's reply.

'But I've done nothing wrong!' the widow cried.

'You pay at once,' he said, 'or else I'll take that brand-new frying-pan to pay the debt you've owed to me since last I summonsed you, and got you off.'

'Liar!' cried the widow. 'I've never had a summons in

my life, and as for you and your frying-pan, the Devil take you both!'

Hearing her curse, the fiend came forward, rubbing his hands with glee:

'Now, now, Mother Mabel, can this be a joke, or do you really mean the things you say?'

'The Devil can have him, pan and all, unless he repents,' she said.

'Do you repent?' the fiend then asked. The Summoner said:

'Not I!'

'Then you and the pan are mine by right,' the fiend exclaimed, 'and you shall be in Hell to-day.'

With that, he swooped and carried off his prey, and the Summoner was never seen again. But the widow lived happily ever after.

The Death of Roland

The Death of Roland

FOR SEVEN LONG YEARS, the Emperor Charlemagne had warred in Spain. No castle, no walled city could withstand the onset of his Frankish chivalry, save only Saragossa, last stronghold of King Marsilius the Saracen. He called a council of his chiefs, and with one voice they urged him to submit to Charlemagne, to offer gifts and hostages for peace. Marsilius chose to be ambassador his wisest counsellor, called Blancandrin, and this man rode into the Frankish camp with gifts of golden besants and wild beasts.

'Great Emperor of the Franks,' said Blancandrin, 'Marsilius sends these tokens of respect. If you will leave this land, he vows that he will come to you at Aix and be baptized, *and* hold his realm as vassal of fair France.'

'The Saracen speaks well,' said Charlemagne. 'Does he speak true?'

'Trust not the Infidel,' brave Roland said, 'have we not found him false for seven years?'

Ganilon, his step-father, stood up, frowning at the son he never loved.

'Give no ear to braggarts,' he advised, and persuaded many peers to sue for peace. Charlemagne agreed:

'But which of you shall meet the Saracen?'

'I would gladly go, Sire,' Roland said.

But Oliver, his friend, said with a smile:

'You are too rash to play ambassador!'

'Then choose my prudent step-sire, Ganilon,' mocked Roland, and the paladins agreed. Ganilon for shame dare not refuse, but swore to be revenged:

'If God grant that I come back safe and sound, I will

[120]

wreak such vengeance, this I swear, as will last you, Roland, all your life!'

He set out for Saragossa with bad grace, and soon caught up the Moorish embassy, on its way back to Marsilius. The cunning Blancandrin said to the Frank:

'How great a king is your lord, Charlemagne. And yet his peers, I think, advise him ill, urging him to battles long and hard.'

Said Ganilon:

'His nephew, Roland, is the man to blame—proud Roland who each day courts his own death. Only when it comes shall we have peace.'

'Can it be so?' said crafty Blancandrin, and other things they said along the way.

Marsilius was enraged when Ganilon gave him the terms of peace from Charlemagne—to yield up half his kingdom, otherwise be led in chains to Aix, and basely slain. He would have killed the Frank but Blancandrin whispered in his master's ear:

'This man has that to say which you should hear.'

Marsilius took Ganilon aside and questioned him on how he might get peace.

'While Roland lives, and his friend Oliver, you never will.'

'How shall we bring this Roland to his death?' Marsilius asked.

'Make peace with Charlemagne, and he will lead his army back to France. Roland will demand to be the last to leave this land. As he and Oliver ride in the rear through the mountain-pass of high Roncevaux, let your men ambush them and so win peace.'

The Death of Roland

Marsilius gave Ganilon much gold and sealed the pact between them to betray Count Roland to his death.

Ganilon reached the Frankish camp again.

'You may trust the Saracens,' he said. A thousand trum pets sounded through the camp the news that the long war was at an end. Before the army marched, the Emperor said:

'But who will stay to guard the rear for us when we cross over the high mountain pass?'

'Choose Roland,' said the treacherous Ganilon, 'no man more fit than he for such a task.'

And so it was that Roland stayed behind, though Charlemagne was loathe to leave him there, and with him all the peers, the flower of France. Slowly in the rear came this brave band, not knowing that Marsilius and his men were stealing on before by secret paths. They came to Roncevaux just at break of day, and Oliver rode up a nearby hill to look around. He saw the sunlight gleam on armoured men and heard the clamour of a mighty host. He galloped back to let Count Roland know what hordes were closing in on every side.

'Heaven grant us battle!' Roland cried. But Oliver was wiser, and he said:

'Treachery is all the cause of this, that we are ambushed now. Companion Roland, sound your horn, I pray, that Charlemagne may hear it from afar and turn to aid us.'

'My fame would be destroyed by such a deed,' Count Roland said. 'Rather will I dye my sword Durendal to the hilt in Paynim blood!'

'Companion Roland, sound your horn, I pray, that Charlemagne may come back in his might.'

'I will not put my family to shame or bring dishonour on the land of France, but with Durendal smite that pagan host,' said Roland angrily.

'Companion Roland, sound your horn, I pray. The Emperor will hear it as he rides.'

'I'll strike a thousand with Durendal's blade before I blow my horn for any foe,' was the reply.

'It would have been no shame,' said Oliver, 'for such a mighty host. Who fights this day will live to fight no more!'

The French knelt for a moment to receive Archbishop Turpin's blessing. He absolved them from their sins—their penance was to strike the Paynim hard! They rose and mounted, rode into the field, shouting the Emperor's war-cry of 'Montjoie!' Fierce was the battle, bold the Frankish knights; the corpses of the Paynims were piled high, but for every one who fell another came. Though Oliver and Roland, and the peers, did wondrous feats of chivalry that day, their numbers dwindled with each passing hour, till there were left no more than sixty knights.

Count Roland cried to Oliver his friend:

'Alas! that we should lose the flower of France. How can we bring the Emperor this news?'

'There is no way,' said Oliver, 'not now. I would rather die than lose renown.'

Said Roland: 'I will sound my horn aloud. Charlemagne will hear and turn again.'

'And shame your family and France?' cried Oliver. 'When I first asked you would not. I say no.'

'This fight is fought with peril,' Roland said. 'I will sound my horn to bring them riding back.'

'When I first asked you would not out of pride,' said Oliver. 'To sound it now would ill befit a knight.'

'Wherefore this rage?' the other asked.

Said Oliver: 'Your rashness is the cause of all our deaths. True valour is not proud foolhardiness. Now is the Emperor Charlemagne bereft of all our strength and France is robbed of her most noble sons. Our friendship ends here on this battlefield. A bitter parting must we have this day.'

Turpin heard their quarrel and drew near: 'Let there be no rage between you two! It will not save the day to sound the horn, yet let its notes ring loud. The King will learn what has become of us, take vengeance for us, give us burial.'

So Roland blew the horn. Its note rang loud; the sound went echoing for thirty leagues, and far away, the Emperor heard its cry.

'Our men have need of us,' said Charlemagne.

'No, no,' said Ganilon, 'that cannot be.'

A second time Count Roland blew the horn with all his might, until the blood came pouring from his mouth.

'I hear the horn of Roland crying out,' said Charlemagne, 'and never would he blow except in battle.'

Ganilon the traitor quickly said: 'He hunts the hare, or sounds it but in jest. Let us ride until we reach fair France.'

And so they rode. A third time Roland blew, so long and hard his temples burst and the bright blood ran down.

'That is the note made with a man's last strength,' said Naimon to the King, so far away. 'The man must be a traitor who denies that he is hearing Roland's last appeal. Shall we not arm and ride back to his aid?'

They armed, and swiftly backwards made their way, praying that they yet might be in time. Ganilon was made a prisoner until events should show where his love lay. High were the hills and huge and shadowy, deep the vales where Frankish trumpets rang. But all too late—they could not come in time.

Roland, on the field of battle, groaned. For what availed the valour of so few? The Saracens redoubled their attack and Oliver received a deadly wound, pierced between the shoulders with a lance. He cried out to Count Roland for his aid. Roland cut his way through savage foes to reach him, but so blinded with his blood was Oliver that he struck wildly out, and clove the golden helm of his own friend. And yet his head was not touched by the blade.

'Oliver! It is Roland that you strike!' he cried.

'Alas!' said Oliver, 'I cannot see, but yet I hear your voice, Roland, forgive me!' And with that he died.

When Roland saw him die, he bade farewell: 'For many a year have we fought side by side. Now you are dead, I do not care to live.'

Of all the Frankish host but three remained—Roland the paladin, Count Walter de Hum and Turpin the Arch-bishop, who that day struck many a valiant blow like any knight. But Walter soon was slain, and Turpin felled, though straight he rose again and fought on foot.

Roland, reeling from the grievous pain which racked his temples, broken by the blast, yet blew again. The sound was faint, but still the Emperor heard, and sixty thousand clarions replied. The hills resounded and the valleys rang. Fear struck cold in every Paynim breast and they resolved to quickly make an end of these last two, before the Emperor came. Now Veillantif was slain—the great war-horse that Roland loved so well. He looked around. The field was strewn with friends. Tears mingled with the blood upon his face. Once more he blew the horn until it cracked. But now the echo from the hills around was taken up and answered by the note of the war-horns of the Frankish host riding through dark valleys into Spain. Roland smiled, and laid his head to rest on the horse that still served him in death. From his weak hand the sword Durendal fell, that had never failed him till this day. As he lay dying, there crept up to his side a Saracen who coveted the sword and would have robbed him of it, had not his eyes then opened. Rising up, he brought his horn down on the Paynim's head, breaking skull and helmet, and the horn which shivered into fragments in his hand. Gathering his last strength, he stood upright, and swung Durendal high above his head. He dashed it on a rock, so that no foe should bear it into battle after him. But yet the bright steel held and clove the rock. He laid the sword beneath him with the shards of that clear horn that would not ring again, as he rode out to fight the Infidel.

With that, Count Roland turned his face to Spain, and died at last, beneath a lonely pine. And there the Emperor found him that same day, when all too late he reached that field of blood. There was no voice to answer when he called for his Twelve Peers, the flower of all France, save vulture's croak and screaming eagle's cry. The Frankish host pur-sued the Saracens and cut them down in flight; long hours they rode and hunted down their prey, for by a miracle the midday sun was halted in the sky and did not set till the road to Saragossa was bestrewn with Paynim dead, the dark vale of Tenebrosa piled up high and Ebro's current choked with drowning men. Fearful was the slaughter that they made before they bore Count Roland back to France. Wild horses were the death of Ganilon for his base deed, yet nothing could assuage the Emperor's grief. He wept for Roland's loss by night and day, and cried aloud:

'Would God that I had died, before I brought such heavy news to France!'

Sir Orfeo

Metrical Romance

ONCE UPON A TIME, there was a king of England who was the best harper in all the world. His name was Orfeo, and he had lived happily with his wife, Heurodis, for many years, when one day a great disaster befell them. It was the month of May, and the fields and woods were fair with blossoms when Heurodis went into the orchard with two of her maidens to hear the birds sing among the branches. They sat down in the shade of an apple-tree for it was midday and the sun was hot. The Queen fell asleep, and the maidens, fearing to wake her, let her sleep on late into the afternoon. When she awoke, it was as if she had had a terrible dream, for she shrieked and rent her clothes, and scratched her fair countenance with her finger-nails. Thinking that she had lost her wits, the maidens ran to the castle for aid, and soon the Queen was being carried to her room, now weeping piteously. Sir Orfeo was summoned and came at once to his wife, alarmed at the change in her.

'Heurodis!' he cried. 'Tell me what has befallen you, that you who were wont to be so quiet and still, make this outcry? Your face is scratched and bleeding, your garments torn—what has so frightened you?'

'Alas! my lord,' wept the Queen, 'as I lay sleeping under the apple-tree, two knights came to me there, who bade me go with them to their king. When I would not, they left me but presently returned in a great company, with a hundred knights and a hundred ladies riding about their king. Their horses and garments were white as snow, and for a crown the king wore no diadem of silver or of gold, but a single precious gem, burning on his brow. Whether I would or

no, he made me accompany them into their own country, a green, flat land of woods and pastures and winding streams. "Here you must dwell forever," said the king, "and there can be no escape. Wherever you may hide, we shall find you. You may return to your own people now to say farewell, but be under the apple-tree tomorrow at noon and we will come for you." And that, my lord, is why I weep, for we must part forever.'

'That shall never be!' exclaimed Sir Orfeo, 'I would rather lose my life than lose my Queen.'

He asked counsel of all his advisers, but there was not one who could help him and at last he had to devise a plan for himself by which he might save her. The next day at noon, when Heurodis lay down beneath the apple-tree, Sir Orfeo led out a thousand knights who made a shield-wall round her, thinking that nothing now could carry her off. But suddenly she vanished from their sight, none knew where.

Great was the sorrow in the castle, for she had been dearly loved, but the greatest sorrow was that of Orfeo.

'Bring me a beggar's garb,' he said, 'for I will lay aside my crown to wander in the wilderness. What is my kingdom to me if I have not my Queen? When I am gone summon Parliament and choose another king.'

The courtiers protested but he would not listen to them, and at last his dearest counsellor consented to rule as Steward in his place until a king were chosen. Then, taking only his harp with him, Orfeo left castle and kingdom to make his home in the forest. He hid the harp in a hollow oak but each day, when the sun arose, he would take it out and play to himself. Birds, hearing a music sweeter than their own, would fly to him and wild beasts creep up to his feet, such sounds of enchantment he drew from those strings. But once he stopped playing, they dared not stay near him for he was a fearsome sight. His clothes were tattered, while his hair and beard had grown down to his waist. Where once he had slept in silken sheets, now he had the hard ground for his bed, and for fare wild herbs and berries. For ten long years he lived thus, and saw no human face. Yet often he would see the King of Fairyland hunting with his men and hear their faint horns blowing, or espy the fairy host marshalling for war, he knew not where, or some company of fairy lords and ladies dancing to pipe and timbrel on the smooth-shaven grass.

Then one day, a troop of sixty fair women came riding by, each with a falcon at her wrist, for they were going hawking along the river-edge. And in their midst was Heurodis! He looked at her, and she at him, but not one word did either speak. Seeing his wild hair and ragged clothes, she began to weep at the change in him, and at once the other ladies pulled her away and rode off into the forest.

'Alas! why may I not die?' grieved Sir Orfeo. 'Too long has my life lasted when I dare not speak one word to my own wife, nor she to me. Yet I will follow her, wherever she may go.'

With this, he ran swiftly after the disappearing company. They rode straight into a rock, and he after them. He found himself inside a tunnel which after three miles or so, as near as he could make it, opened out into a broad fair country, smooth and flat, with not a hill or dale in sight. In the midst of this land, there stood a royal castle with a hundred battlemented towers. Its walls were of crystal and from the moat sprang glittering golden buttresses; its spacious halls were built with precious stones and the meanest pillar in it was of gold. It was never dark in that land, for when it should have been night the jewelled stones shone bright as the noonday sun. At this castle the ladies alighted, and Sir Orfeo followed them in. He knocked at the gate, and when the porter asked him what he wished, he replied:

'I am a harper and have come to play before your king.'

The porter let him in at once, for the fairy king loved nothing more than music. Looking about him, Orfeo saw, inside the wall, all the people who were thought to have died, but had really been carried off by the fairies. They looked just as they had done at the moment of their disappearance; some knights were sitting on horseback, fully-armed, but a great many lay as if resting at noon, for that was a most magic time, and if perchance you lay then under an apple-tree, the fairies would be sure to take you. As each one was when the fairies seized him, so was he when they brought him here, and Orfeo saw his wife lying under her apple-tree. He knew her by her clothes.

When he had seen all this, he went to the king, and knelt before him, saying:

'My lord, if it be your will, hear my minstrelsy.'

'What manner of man are you?' asked the king, 'I did not send for you. Never before has it happened that a man has come to my realm unbidden.'

'Sire, I am only a wandering minstrel in search of fame and fee. Many a lord's house I seek, even if unwelcome, for that is the custom of my kind.'

And, taking up his harp, he began to play. Fairies though

they were, they had never heard music of such sweetness, surpassing even the songs of elves. All the castle came to hear him, and when he had finished playing the king sighed, and said:

'Harper, your music has greatly pleased me. Ask of me any reward you wish and I will give it gladly.'

'Then give me the lady who lies beneath the apple-tree.'

'Ask anything but that!' cried the king, 'an ill pair you would make—you so rough and she so fair. Hateful would it be to see you in her company!'

'More hateful still for a king to break his word,' said Sir Orfeo.

'Since it must be so,' said the king, 'take her by the hand and lead her hence.'

Orfeo knelt and said his thanks, then leading Heurodis by the hand he made his long way back through the rock and into his own land.

When he came to the city, he went first to the cottage of a poor man by the city-gates, asking shelter there and news of the kingdom. The man told him how the Queen had been carried off by fairies ten long years ago, how the king in his grief had wandered off into the wilderness none knew where, and how the Steward governed the land, still waiting for his lord's return, though time and again the barons had urged him to take the crown for himself. Hear-ing this, Sir Orfeo left Heurodis at the cottage and went into the city, still clad in his beggar's rags so that none should recognize him. There in the street he met the Steward, and called out loudly to him:

'Sir Steward, I am a harper come from a distant land. Help me now in my distress!'

[135]

The Steward replied:

'Come with me. Of whatever I have, you shall have part, for the sake of my lord, Sir Orfeo. Every harper is welcome in his name.'

They went to the castle, and there in the great hall, when everyone had fallen silent after the meal, Orfeo took his harp and played upon it. The Steward recognized it at once.

'Tell me, minstrel,' he cried, 'where you came by this harp?'

'Once, in an unknown land, I passed through a barren wilderness and there in a valley I found a man torn by lions and devoured by wolves. Beside him lay this harp.'

'Alas!' cried the Steward, 'that I should live to hear these tidings. What shall become of me, now that I have lost so good a lord?'

The barons tried to comfort him, but it was of no avail. Then Sir Orfeo knew that his Steward was loyal and true, and gently he said:

'Sir Steward, if I were King Orfeo and had endured much hardship in the wilderness before I won my Queen back from the fairies, and if I had left her at the edge of town while I came here to try your loyalty, and if I had found you true, you should never forget it. But if you had rejoiced at my death, you would have lost your office and my love.'

Then the Steward knew that his lord had returned to him, and he fell at Orfeo's feet, laughing and weeping at once in his joy. Swiftly the courtiers led Sir Orfeo to his chamber, and bathed him, trimmed his wild hair, and attired him as a king. Heurodis was brought to the castle with much rejoicing, and Orfeo newly crowned with his Queen beside him. They ruled together many a long year and after them, the Steward was made king, in reward for his loyalty and his love.

About these Stories

About these Stories

¶ *Romances*

For most people, the words 'Middle Ages' conjure up a picture of gallant knights rescuing damsels in distress or riding out on a perilous quest, to hunt a dragon and kill a giant or two. This is because medieval people loved stories of such things. They are called 'Romances' and there are a great many of them. The ones in this collection are all about knights, it is true, but the other ingredients which went into each can be very different. To understand why this should be so, we must look at some of the other kinds of literature which were popular then.

¶ *Stories of knightly deeds.* 'Chansons de Gestes' ('Songs of Deeds'), is the name given to a group of story-poems written in French, which were almost wholly concerned with knights and battles. The earliest and most famous of these is the 'Song of Roland'. Our story the *Death of Roland,* is a very short summary of this poem. It was written at the end of the eleventh century but there were already many stories of Charlemagne and his Twelve Peers, of the friendship of Roland and Oliver, and of the treachery of Ganilon. These were all based on an event which took place in the year 777, when Charlemagne abandoned an expedition into Spain. As he was re-passing the Pyrenees, his rearguard was attacked and destroyed by Saracens, the Arabic invaders who conquered Spain. Among those who fell was a certain 'Roland, duke of the marches of Brittany'. This is about all we know of the man who was to become such a great hero.

Some romances are like the Chansons de Gestes in that they concern themselves chiefly with knightly deeds. *The Knight with the Two Swords* centres on the tragic situation

which arises when two knights fail to recognize each other.
It is indeed, only the main plot of *The Book of Balin* in
which Balin has many different adventures before he meets
Balan again, but it shows the sort of skeleton which
romances had before the magic and marvels were added.
Little is known of its author, Sir Thomas Malory, except
that he was a knight of Warwickshire who spent several
years in prison and died in 1471. We do not know if the
charges made against him were true or false, whether he
was a great rogue or an innocent victim. But we do know
that while he was in prison, he wrote a series of stories about
King Arthur and his knights, which William Caxton
later printed under the title of *Le Morte d'Arthur*. The
Book of Balin is the second story in Caxton's edition; it is
complete in itself and Arthur plays only a very small part
in it, but Malory wove it into the fabric of the history of the
Round Table by means of the sub-plots. It is one of the few
of our stories which were written in prose and not poetry, but
it is such beautiful prose that you really cannot tell the differ-
ence.

The French romance *The Dragon of Rhodes* is also concerned with the actions and ideals of knights. In *The
Death of Roland*, Oliver pointed out that simple bravery did
not make a good knight, and in this story, Theodore has to
learn that a knight's first duty is not to achieve fame, but to
keep his promises. The importance of keeping promises
is the mainspring of the action in *Sir Gawain and the
Green Knight* too. Gawain is a very good knight, but
not quite perfect, because he breaks his promise to Bercilak in the hope of saving his own life. But *Sir Gawain*
combines all three of the main themes of romance, and

we shall return to it when we have considered the other two.

¶ *Stories of love.* It was only in the twelfth century that poets began to think that love was as good a subject for their poems as war had always been. One of the first people to write love-stories was Marie de France, a poetess who probably belonged to an aristocratic French family living in England. At some time before 1189, she wrote twelve short poems known as 'lays'. In *The Two Lovers*, she uses the old folk-tale of the *Perilous Princess* whose hand can only be won if her suitor passes a severe test. It usually has a happy ending but Marie turns it into a tragedy. Like Roland, the young man is too proud to accept help and so perishes. *The Nightingale* is also sad, for it tells the story of a lady who is married to a cruel, old baron and falls in love with a gay, young one. Many of the love-stories of the Middle Ages have sad endings, usually because the lady was married to someone else. In those days people could not often marry whom they wanted, but those whom their parents chose, and the choice was not always a good one. Marie's sad pair remind us of Lancelot and Guinevere, of Tristram and Iseult.

A happy ending is given to *Aucassin and Nicolette*, a story of young love. Here it is the hero's father who tries to prevent the match because he thinks that Nicolette is only a slave-girl. The love-sickness of medieval lovers is often taken to ridiculous lengths. They have been described, in words borrowed from *Alice*, as 'reeling, writhing and fainting in coils'! Aucassin does not actually swoon from love as others do, but if it had been left to him, the story might not have had such a happy ending. Fortunately for

About these Stories

him, he had the brave, practical and resourceful Nicolette
to sort out their problem.

❡ *Stories of magic.* The lays of Marie de France are usually
called 'Breton lays' because she claimed that her plots all
came from Breton minstrels. Now the Bretons were not
French but Celts like the Welsh, and these stories all spring
from Celtic legend, which abounds in marvels and enchant-
ments. *The Three Plagues of Britain* is a straightforward
fairy-tale taken from the *Mabinogion,* a collection of
Welsh stories written down in the *White Book of
Rhydderch* in the early fourteenth century and in the *Red
Book of Hergest* in the latter part of the same century. The
stories themselves must date from a time well before these
manuscripts, however. Many of the romances add the Celtic
fairy-world to that of human love and war. The result is
stories like *Sir Launfal* and *Sir Orfeo.* The earliest version of
Sir Launfal is in fact one of Marie's Breton lays, but ours is
taken from the English verse-romance of the late fourteenth
century in which it is claimed that 'Thomas Chestre made
þys tale'. We know nothing about Thomas Chestre but
his poem is much simpler than Marie's, and it seems clear
that he was writing not for some court, as she was, but for
the common people, who would assemble in a market-
place or inn-yard to hear it recited.

French poets were referring to a lay of Orfeo even before
1200, but our version was written in English in the early
fourteenth century. You will recognize it as the Greek
legend of Orpheus, the Thracian harper who descended
into Hades to look for his dead wife, Eurydice. He was
allowed to lead her back into the world of the living but
told not to turn round before he crossed the borders of

[143]

Hades or she would vanish. He forgot the command, looked round to see if she were following and so lost her forever. This story passed into the Middle Ages by way of the Roman poets Vergil and Ovid, and the sixth century writer Boethius. The Bretons turned Orpheus into a knight and Hades into the Celtic fairy-land. The English writer even makes him a king of England and identifies Thrace with Winchester! Most important of all, the story is given a happy ending.

The Loathly Lady is a fairy-tale of this Celtic type as told by the poet Chaucer in his *Canterbury Tales*. We shall learn a bit more about Chaucer later. Perhaps the most beautiful of all English romances is *Sir Gawain and the Green Knight*. It combines our three main ingredients—love, brave deeds and magic, and it is much better written than most romances into the bargain. The author is unknown but he must have been writing at about the same time as Chaucer in the second half of the fourteenth century, and these two men are the greatest of English medieval poets. The author of *Gawain* has taken two Celtic themes, the Beheading Game and the Temptation by the Lady, and combined them by making the outcome of the first dependant on the knight's resistance to the second. He writes in the vigorous dialect of North-western England, and has a special flair for description, seen at its best in the accounts of the Green Knight's appearance and Gawain's armour, of the castle of Bercilak and the winter journey, of the three hunts and the many feasts. I can only tell you the outline of the story—I cannot show you how great a poet the author was.

About these Stories

❡ Animal Fables
Of course medieval people liked other things beside romances. They were very fond of fables too. These are stories in
which the characters are not people but animals. You must
all know the story of *The Goose that laid the Golden eggs*
and *The Town Mouse and the Country Mouse*. These
two are to be found in the collection known as *Aesop's
Fables*. Aesop is supposed to have been a Phrygian slave
who lived in the sixth century B.C. so you can see that fables
have been popular for a long time. In the Middle Ages
there was a very famous collection of stories about Renart, or
as we call him, Reynard the Fox. It was called *Le Roman
de Renart* but was not a romance at all. It consists of
separate stories written by different people between 1175
and 1250. The aim of the authors was not to depict animals
as such, but through them to criticize the faults of men.
Renart is a crafty rogue, Chanticleer a braggart, Ysengrin a
rather dull clod. I have taken the story of *How Ysengrin the
Wolf was taught to fish* straight from the French 'Roman'
but *The Tale of Chanticleer* is Chaucer's version of the story
of the cock and the fox. No one else tells it so well or makes
such a lively character of the cock himself.

❡ Moral Tales
In the Middle Ages, people had a great liking for stories
with a particular point or moral. Since Chaucer tells such
stories much better than anyone else in English, all three of
our moral tales are taken from his great poem 'The Canterbury Tales'. Chaucer was born in about the year 1340,
and after being trained as a page in the household of one of
the royal princes, he finally became a courtier and diplomat.

About these Stories

Edward III once referred to him as 'our dearly beloved valet' and employed him on several foreign missions. He rose steadily in what we should call the Civil Service, except for a spell of three years when his patron, John of Gaunt, was abroad and could not secure posts for him. He died in 1400 and was buried in Westminster Abbey. The tomb built for him in the fifteenth century by an admirer was the first of those in Poets' Corner. It is not known when he began writing poetry. He complained that as he got older he found it more and more difficult to write, and he left *The Canterbury Tales* unfinished when he died. It is a collection of stories in verse, set in the framework of a pilgrimage to Canterbury. According to the Prologue, he intended to make each pilgrim tell two stories on the journey from London to Canterbury, and two on the way back. There were many collections of tales written at about this time but only Chaucer had the idea of choosing ones to suit their tellers. *The Loathly Lady* for instance, which is about who should have the 'maisterie', the upper hand in marriage, is given to the Wife of Bath, a very merry widow, who has buried five husbands and is now looking for a sixth. She firmly believed that men should be kept in their place!

The Three Young Men and Death, the first of our moral tales, is told by the Pardoner, a man who sold forgiveness of sins, as if such a thing could be sold! The tale of the three men who did not recognize Death in their own greed for gold, is given point in the framework of the pilgrimage because its teller is himself the most avaricious person there. Moreover, he says before he begins that he is going to tell the sort of story he uses to frighten people so much that they

About these Stories

are ready to pay anything for forgiveness. The pilgrims laugh at the time at the foolishness of such people, but by the end of the Pardoner's story they are so taken in that they do exactly the same thing.

The Devil and the Summoner is a moral story of the kind known as satire. It points out the defects of a certain type of person but instead of simply denouncing them, makes them ridiculous. Just as the Pardoner made money out of people's fear of Hell, so the Summoner made his out of their fear and ignorance of the Law. The only pilgrim who did not enjoy hearing how one rogue at least got his deserts, was the real Summoner who was travelling with them!

The Alchemist is another satire, and is one of the few Canterbury Tales which are believed to have been invented by Chaucer. In those days, people set less store on telling new stories than on telling the old ones even better than before. This is certainly one of Chaucer's best works. Alchemists were forerunners of our scientists, but they were only trying to solve one problem—how to turn base metals into gold. They never succeeded of course, but there were impostors among them who, like the Canon, managed to persuade simple-minded folk that they had.

About the Author

JENNIFER WESTWOOD is now working for a Ph.D. at Cambridge in England and has been a full-time student for the past six years. She took her B.A. at St. Anne's College, Oxford, where she studied medieval English language and literature. Originally Mrs. Westwood went to Cambridge to study archaeology but "hated the bones and things," so transferred to the Anglo-Saxon tripos (honors course). She is now preparing an edition of a late medieval Icelandic romance entitled *The Story of Nikulas the Jester.*

not reviewed